SIMPLE ANNALS

Roy Watkins was born near Southport, Lancashire, in December 1939. After spending the early war years with his Welsh grandparents in Liverpool, he was carried back to his birthplace by his mother to escape the Blitz.

He ran the gamut of the local school system (Junior, Secondary, Technical, and Grammar), and left Southport to go to Hull University in 1959. He proved to be a poor academic, but a good writer and a good teacher.

In 1966, Faber & Faber published some of his short stories, after which he taught in secondary schools, then left England for the USA to attend Columbia University Graduate School of Arts, where he mended his academic reputation.

After teaching at various universities for several years, he moved to Wales with his wife, Eve. They became deeply involved in family history research, and also founded a letterpress publishing concern, Embers Handpress, printing and binding books of poetry and translation by hand.

He retired in 2014, and now lives in Northern France.

ROY WATKINS

Simple Annals

A memoir of early childhood

Author's note: The names of my family members and two of my schoolteachers are taken from the life. The names of all other characters are fictitious.

First published in 2021
by CB editions
146 Percy Road London W12 9QL
www.cbeditions.com

Frontispiece: drawing of the Fog Bell by J. L. Watkins

The right of Roy Watkins to be identified as author
of this work has been asserted in accordance
with the Copyright, Designs and Patents Act, 1988

Printed in England by Blissetts, London W3 8DH

ISBN 978–1–909585–39–3

To all families
where love lives in memory

THE FIRST PART

213 Lytham Road, Marshside

1

The intimacy of toys when it's raining...A cardboard sweetshop with labels on shiny tin bottles; a little lead Red Indian, kneeling with a raised tomahawk; a white, four-engined bomber in a cardboard hangar; the Child's Bible with stand-up figures; words, the magic shapes of letters on pages not understood – they are the doors: they open one by one on different worlds that are themselves and the same world.

The *hush*...going from room to room at Aunty Mary's when nobody's home. Cousin Eric looks for fingerprints, I look for treasure – into cupboards and corners, over eiderdowns, under musty beds: we always find the same things – coats and boots and old gloves, silence and darkness, Grandad's fiddle, and the family Bible under a big, quiet bed.

The moment after each peal of thunder leaves me giddy with stillness, curled up on Aunty Mary's dusty sofa under the window – maroon velvet, smell of sleep.

'Nah we can do owt we want!' Eric says, and pees seriously into the fire.

∾

Aunty Mary and Aunty Kitty sing a duet. We're in the back kitchen. Aunty Mary looks shy – she always does – she's wearing that long, blue coat with rabbit collars. Aunty Kitty wears two cardigans, one over the other, she's always cold, she was born cold Grandma says... and she should know, she says, since she sleeps every night in the same bed with her. 'Come on, Mary, shake a leg!' she says, and so they link arms, and I wonder ever after why they link arms when they're supposed to shake a leg:

> *Show me the way to go 'ome*
> *I'm tired and I want to go to bed*
> *I 'ad a little drink about an ower a... go*
> *And it went right to my 'ead...*
> *SO...*
> *Show me the way to go 'ome...*

'What's next, Kitty?'
'Eh?'
'I said what's next...'
'How should I know!'

They don't finish. They never finish. I'm glad. They always laugh, but back behind them in the song, they're sad... Those songs are sad, I know, I know... there's sommat behind them, shadows creeping up, enough to make you weep.

∾

It's different when Grandma sings. Hymns every night. Songs sometimes, not often. Not like Aunty Kitty, something from the Hit Parade, never *Would You Rather Be a Fish*.

Sometimes she sings *When Grandpa Papered the Parlour*, but that's not real singing, or else *The Grand Old Duke of York*, and she marches up and down the kitchen with her rolling pin over her shoulder. I don't know who he was, the Duke of York, but I just lie there and listen. One day, half way through kneading dough, she suddenly tilts her face up and sings –

> *All the birds of the air come a-sighing and a-sobbing*
> *When they heard of the death of poor cock robin*
> *When they heard . . .*
> *Of the death . . .*
> *Of poor . . .*
> *Cock . . .*
> *Robin . . .*

She sang that, I think, to make the bread rise: flour-dust on her pinnie whitening her hair. She looks sad, stomps round the kitchen, chucks coal on the fire, goes back to her dough.

'What's matter, Grandma?' I ask.

'Nowt!' she snaps . . . 'Poor cock robin . . .'

∾

. . . *Rockall, Shannon, Lundy, Irish Sea* . . .

These are the words that tuck them up, Mam, Grandma, Aunty K, tuck them up in silence, into their eyes.

I think the words are the waves. It's the shipping forecast. Then the Irish Mail goes over ...

... tap tap ... scrat scrat ...

What's that? Grandma grabs the poker.

It's nowt but a tramp. Poor soul. She finds a bit of bread, bit of mousetrap, a tomato. Not easy on rations. He whispers *Thank you kindly, misses* into his beard. Gone! Gone to a hedge!

... scrat scrat ... tap ... tap ... tap ...

What's that? Grandma grabs the poker.

Nobody. Just wind. Nobbut wind.

'I wish it were our John!' says Grandma.

'Wish it were Bob!' says Mam.

I wish, I wish. I don't know what I wish.

Wish it were wind.

Wish I never had to cry.

ॐ

Aunty Mary's got a job making butter. She swings the handle round all morning, round and round, hour after hour. It's hard work, a wooden churn. At last she gives a little grin and winks, runs her finger round the brim: 'Nearly there!' she says.

Then she gets a job making lead soldiers. That's better! We can have as many as we want. She chucks the lumps of lead into a little pot and holds it with long pincers over the fire. It's almost no-time, the twinkling of an eye. The lumps of lead fall over and there's a shimmering sea.

She makes rugs out of potato sacks and old coats – rag rugs she calls them. They're everywhere, everywhere you look, funny little rugs, all shapes and sizes, dark dingy colours full of dust...

'We know what we'll get for Christmas!' Grandma says.

∾

'My, Mary, this pie's 'ard!' Uncle Hugh says. He's been sawing at it with the breadknife, but it doesn't budge.

'Gie it a swipe, Dad!' Eric says, so Uncle Hugh lifts the breadknife up above his head then stabs the pie right through the middle. Half hits the cat and half flies through the window. Then the parrot claps. We watch the empty air where the pie has flown.

'Good job you didn't ate it!' Eric says.

Uncle Hugh's birthday, that was.

He was in trouble, Uncle Hugh. His billy goat got loose on the sea bank, and he had to go to court.

'Why, Mam?' Eric said. 'What happened?'

'Shurrup about that!' Aunty Mary said, 'It's nowt but manderous blabbermuck. D'you hear me?' *Manderous blabbermuck!*

Eric's mouth dropped open. 'But Mam, what's that?'

Aunty Mary slowly wagged her finger in the air and screwed her eyes up: 'It's lay-ers to catch meddlers, that's what it is, lay-ers...to catch...MEDDLERS! Nah leave me alone wi' it!'

'Oh! Bloomin' eck!' Eric said.

5

Mam stands at the top of the stairs, I look up at her. Then Mam stands at the bottom of the stairs and I look down at her. 'Mam,' I say, 'who's my mother?'

'Don't be silly!' she says. 'I'm your mother, of course.'

'How many mothers have I got?'

She can't answer. She doesn't know. I know. I've got two. One at the bottom of the stairs and one at the top. Which is the best? That's the trouble. I don't know. Which is the one who turns into the witch? Nobody can tell. That's the trouble. That's the trouble. If I go up towards her, she might turn into the witch. If I go down towards her, she might still turn into the witch. So should I go up or should I go down?

That's the trouble.

'I don't know!' she says, 'I can't fathom him at all! If he goes on at this rate, we'll have to get t'doctor to him...'

'Doctor be damned!' Grandma says.

There are three ways to leave the house – through the back kitchen door into the back yard by the water tank and down the back garden to the plank fence where the elderberry tree hangs over from Aunty Mary's garden, or down the gloomy hall by the stairs and through the front door and then down the front path to the gate, or else out of the back kitchen door into the back yard by the water tank and through the yard gate into the alley and then to the front path and the front gate. These are the three ways to leave the house. But when I go into the street, or else climb through the fence into Aunty Mary's garden, I forget about that.

The mad girl comes along the bank. Always the same. She dances everywhere, wiggling her fingers, holds her hands up and wiggles her fingers like little twigs. This is how she goes:...*dancy dancy dancy*...*wriggle wriggle wriggle*...After a few more wriggles her knickers fall down, some colour or other. Blue this time. She picks 'em up and chucks 'em away, lifts her skirt up...right UP...another pair underneath, green this time. Then again...purple!

'Show me your wee wee, boy,' she says. 'Show me or we'll have to wrestle.'

No use to wrestle. She's too good.

'It's big!' she says. Then off she trots, picking 'em up as she goes, purple, blue, green, turns round and sticks her tongue out, then off.

When I tell Eric, he flies into a rage. 'SHE'S MAD!' he shouts. 'She'll go on like that all year, show me this, show me that! Don't show her owt. And don't look at her knickers, whatever colour she wears. They're the angels of damnation. You can go to Hell for that!'

'What shall I do?' I ask him.

'Get some clogs and gie her a good kicking!'

'Got no clogs...'

'Run off then,' he says. 'How can *she* run, wi' her knickers alus falling down!'

∾

On summer afternoons, I squat on the pavement on the corner of our cul-de-sac where the tar melts, and make tar marbles. I keep an eye on the mongol boy across the road. Grandma leans against the hedge, face tilted into the sun, hands propped in the pockets of her flowered pinnie. The mongol boy lets out a bellow then reaches after it. He wraps his arms round the air, trying to catch his voice. When somebody walks past, he sticks his long arms through the gate and grabs them. He won't let loose. 'Say sommat to him!' Grandma shouts. 'He likes to listen to folk talk...'

He never lets loose till his mam comes out with the belt. 'Let go!' she shouts. 'Let loose of him!' And she whacks him with the belt, pretending to beat him till he runs off with his arms over his head, crying. Then she smiles at Grandma. Swings the belt. But she didn't beat him. Never touched him really. Just pretended, Grandma says.

Later on, shankers come back off the marshes. Horses plod on, taking their time. In every cart, a mound of shrimps writhe and hiss. The shankers sprawl in their seats between the great wheels – Nicky Brid, Tom Scrat, Mucky Bob – their nets dangle behind, stretched over long poles... 'Throw us a shrimp, Nicky Brid!' Grandma shouts. He leans back and sticks his hand into the pink hill of living shrimps then flings it up into the air, and shrimps come pattering around our feet. Grandma gathers them into her pinnie. O Grandma, their whiskers twitch!

'Quick!' she says. 'Ne'er mind about that! Get t' kettle on!'

∽

Eric comes to see me after school. He tells me stories. One day he says: 'Me dad went to catch rats wi' an 'ammer. 'e squats dahn o'er t'rat 'ole an' waits. But t'rat comes aht at t'other 'ole and bites 'im in't bum...ha ha...Then, when e's on 'is way 'ome on t'bus, t' rat jumps aht of 'is pants...'

Uncle Hugh had a long war against rats, and he had a treasure, found it in a barn. Three cocoa tins full of silver thre'penny bits. 'Eric,' I plead, 'let's dig in barns, let's dig in barns for treasure!'

'No good,' he says. 'Me dad's dug it up. Nowt left.'

'Eric, I'll tell you a story.'

'Go on,' he says.

'Grandad won a phonograph...'

'Go on,' he says.

'...won it in a competition...'

'Go on,' he says.

'Postman ran all the way from Southport in the middle of the night with his shirt tails hanging out and wagging in the wind shouting, Dick Howard's won a phonograph...'

'Go on,' he says.

'That's all,' I say.

'I know about that,' he says. 'But you've forgotten sommat. When he knocked on the door, Grandma said why can't he wait till morning like other postmen? *That's* the whole story.'

'Eric, who sings in Heaven?'

That makes him think. He thinks it's a trick, but it's not. That's my trick.

'Angels,' he says. 'Why?'

I know it's Grandad sings in Heaven. Aunty Kitty told

me. Then he drinks his tea with lots of sugar in, because there's no ration books in Heaven.

'Is Grandad an angel, Eric?'

We kick in the dirt among the nettles on the old sea bank. We're looking for fishing hooks. Shankers drop them there, and there's nowt wrong wi' 'em Eric says…Drop them in the nettles, rusty, but that's no matter.

'That's rum!' he says. 'Grandad an angel.' He starts to chuckle. Grandad an angel. Grandad angel on his bike, sit-up-and-beg, Grandad angel winding up his phonograph, *When grandpa papered the parlour*… Laughing more and more, he falls over so I do the same. We laugh a long time in the nettles, till he sits up and rubs his eyes: '*I wonder if he's put soap in their sandwiches yet,*' he says.

There's a long rigmarole about a parrot. It was Eric's parrot, and it died and went to Heaven. Aunty Mary flushed it down the lav. We watched for three days, but it didn't come up again.

∾

Grandma's aspidistra's dying. *Quick!* Fetch Uncle Hugh! He's coming in a minute, coming in a sec. He drags a chair out into the hall and sits there in the gloom, stroking the withered leaves. Then he sticks his fingers into the pot, moves the earth round a bit.

'Thee're! It'll be aw reet nah,' he says. 'It weren't set reet.'

He's lucky, Uncle Hugh. When we go to chapel, he goes to his greenhouse. Aunty Mary grins: 'His chapel's the greenhouse!' she says. 'He sits there, sermonising lettuce.'

I'd like my own chapel, too. But cut grass, not lettuce. New-mown hay. Something nice to roll around in. Something to smell. Not Sunday clothes! Not preaching!

∞

Uncle Dick lives in a warehouse in Preston. We have to go. Grandma doesn't want us to. It's too far, too many air raids, blackout . . . Mam laughs. It's only twenty miles!

'It's only right he should know his uncle,' she says.

'Do as you think best!' says Grandma.

There's a story about Uncle Dick, too. I can see it in the light of Eric's telling. Uncle Dick's on the stage. He has to recite *The Boy Stood on the Burning Deck*, but he's forgotten the words. They're all looking at him, so he has to say sommat for them, and he said:

> *The boy stood on the burning deck*
> *And very nearly slips.*
> *The muscles in his brawny arms*
> *Stood out like fish and chips . . .*

The headmaster comes up on the stage waving his arms. He sends for his cane and he gives Uncle Dick a walloping in front of everybody, even Grandma. She doesn't like that, of course. Grandad says, 'Nah, Lizzie, don't mek a scene!'

'Scene?' she says. 'Scene be damned!' And she struts up onto the stage. She grabs the cane out of his hand and throws it down with a clatter. 'I didn't bring childer into this world to be threatened by t'likes o' thee!' she says. 'What's use o' poetry? What's use on it? Tha can't ate it!

Tha can't pay t'rent wi' it! And they won't tek it in t'pawn-shop.'

And then she gave him a clout round the lug-hole.

(O yes! But she recites the Psalms of David by heart!)

He met us at the bus station. This is a bus station. I've never seen one before. 'Careful!' he says, crossing. He speaks silky soft and his glance goes around me. I know I like him. 'Hello Peg... Hello Roy...' he says. Like a duster over dark wood.

'He lives in a warehouse, your Uncle Dick,' Mam says. 'That's because he's an upholsterer.'

On the bus she said: Always my favourite... Always something nice for me... Never came home without sommat in his pocket...

Now his lights don't work. A warehouse, a huge, dark warehouse full of sofas, and the lights don't work. He points up. The string broke. There used to be a string. Now he has to take a run up a pile of sofas and grab the bit of string that's left. He gets it on the third go. Dust rises in a dense cloud. A light comes on, a single bare bulb shining down on Uncle Dick's bald head.

'Nah we can have a cup o' tea!' he says.

Back home, I can't wait to tell Eric. I know where Uncle Dick hides his money. Sofas make good hiding places, that's why he has them. That's why an upholsterer needs a warehouse.

'I know what you're thinking,' Eric says, 'but you're wrong! Upholstery just means stuffing old sofas, it's got nowt to do wi' holdups. There's no money in them sofas. Only dust.'

～

Too soft when Mam puts me to bed, too soft. She turns the gas low, puts things in drawers, softly. While her back's turned, shadows come slinking into the corners. She doesn't know they're there. If I tell her, she'll say don't be daft. She'll say there's nowt there, just a little shadow when the gas drops. Doesn't matter, that's what she says. *You have to go to sleep, you can't sleep with the light on*...But I don't mind the light, it makes the shadows stay in corners. Don't be daft, she says. Moves soft as a ghost. *Good night*...

Mam goes down, landing gas pops out...A long time, now, till Grandma comes to bed, a long time to fight off the furniture, the things I can't say, the things that hide. I fight them with my eyes. They daren't move while I'm watching.

I hear everything. I hear for miles and miles. I can hear everything that ever happened. Some nights, the fog bell. That's all right if the ships are safe. It's the drummer I can't abide. I say it in my prayers, *Please not the drummer*, but that makes no difference. He's far off when I first hear him, over the stile at the sea bank, and slowly he comes closer, closer and louder, down the grass track between the cornfields, beating a drum as he comes along.

I don't know him. He's drowned probably, a sailor from a wreck, a shanker with his mouth full of sand and seaweed. Or he's the man from the sewage plant that got dragged into the machine. He came out like mincemeat, Eric said. Stands to reason he'd come back, looking for the bits they couldn't find, beating his drum to make folk keep their doors shut.

Louder it came, all the way, right past our windows. Me, I went small, got lost like a needle. *He* was like chalk.

Then morning – white ceiling, emptiness, wind in the net curtains. *I'm alive!*

∾

Grandad came home on leave. He'd brought something out of Heaven in his suitcase. It was one of those suitcases from under my bed. Nobody seemed to care; they ignored him. He just stood there by the kitchen table looking sorry for himself. When he opened his suitcase, it was full of snakes.

'I don't like Heaven!' I say.

'I don't know, I'm sure!' Mam says. 'What am I to do wi' him?'

'Do nowt!' says Grandma. 'It's only divilment!'

'Heaven's full of snakes...'

'Just listen! Listen to him!'

'Don't worry, Peg,' says Aunty Mary. 'Our Eric's just same, alus talking about t'colour of his business!'

I keep a certain look on my face, a very knowing look. It means that I know what matters. I'm thinking about all the cockroaches dead inside the piano, in the green powder, waiting in Heaven to get their own back.

'It's under the bed!' I say.

Clues. Never the obvious. The obvious hurts too much, leaves nothing to hide in.

When Doctor Lyle asked me what time it was, I held up my toy watch. Why did *he* want to know what time it was? He had a watch of his own. So I thought: I'll tell you what time it is when Nelson gets his eye back! I lay in wait for him in the long grass outside ... *When Nelson gets his eye back!*

I saw his legs go past but didn't shout. After all, he'd have known it was Grandma who said *When Nelson gets his eye back.*

But I thought it hard.

It's a change that happens when the door shuts. In the bath, for example. I kneel with my boats – gaslight in the eerie bathroom. Mam goes out to get on with her supper. Door closes. *There ...* It's not the same, is it? There's another sort of light that's in me. It turns on when doors shut.

Then I start seeing things – *myself ...* my arm, my hand, my leg, my knee, no matter what I do I see them, arm, hand, leg, knee – myself – and boats and water rocking, won't stop still, can't make the rocking stop ... I try hard, hard as I can, but the light sets, turns cruel around me, and the water moves, makes me feel sick ...

I stop breathing. *No, not really.* It's a joke, isn't it?

No. I'm scared. That's why I shout, 'Mam, I'm lonely!' Just a minute. Just a minute. *What's a minute?* Why won't they come? I'm scared to see this ...

That's when Aunty Kitty pops her nose in. The other light goes off, disappears – I breathe ...

'Need a soaping, do you?' she says, starting a lather. 'Come on, come on ...' Right in my mouth! She never misses.

Then what? Do we laugh? Yes, but I say I'm sorry to the echoes.

∾

In my dream, Grandad's photo's on the wall. I take it down and pull the back off in case he's hiding in the wad of brown paper. There never was a photo of Grandad, except the snapshot on Grandma's dresser. There were only two pictures: *Ruth Gleaning in the Fields of Boaz*, and an oil painting of Mary Price, Grandma's mother who came from Flint, wearing a black, black dress and sitting on Aunty Mary's sofa with a gold chain round her neck.

She's in another dream, because of her finger. You can see in the picture that she's getting ready to point. I don't like that. Then Aunty K comes in to say goodnight. I can't speak. 'Are you scared, love?' she asks. 'Is it the furniture?' *She knows!* I nod frantically. She throws her head back and laughs. 'O that's nowt to worry about! We'll soon take care o' that!' she says, and she opens the window wide and begins to throw the furniture out.

'Is that a' right now, love?' I nod again and she goes towards the door.

That's when *she* unfolds her arms and points. She points at me. That's when I realise that she's the boss. I'm too afraid to speak. Aunty K is going out, her fingers are sliding away off the doorknob and the door is closing, and the skin of Aunty Kitty's hand is turning old like paint, cracking and peeling, and the other finger, *her* finger, is coming back to life...

'That's mummy black,' somebody says, nodding at Mary Price. 'The paint, I mean...made from Egyptian mummies.'

'Don't be morbid!' Grandma says. 'It's my mother. A good likeness, and a good woman!'

With furniture, every word is a bite that leaves darkness after it.

The corner gas-lamp hisses, just hisses.

This is a different kind of darkness, one that keeps the light on. That's what the mirror says, *leave the light*... the mirror likes the light: and then the speaker gets ready for a word. It's the wardrobe this time, looks innocent like ordinary wood, like door handles. And perhaps this time it *will* be darkness – BITE it goes, speaking with its silence, BITE, BITE...

Who cares, who cares... That's what the stairs say, sneering.

∾

Longing, looking at the ceiling: an ache that blooms inside like hunger.

'Grandma, I want something...'

'Sommat t'ate?' she says. I think of every possible thing to eat and it's not there.

'No...'

'Sommat to drink, then?'

Perhaps, but... 'No, it's nowt to drink...'

'Tha can shurrup about it then, there's nowt else!' she says, settling down with her book.

'Grandma, what is there I've never had?'

'O, do stop tormentin', there's a good lad!'

It must be something or I wouldn't want it, but I don't know where to look. *It's the thing that matters.*

'Grandma... it's *important*... is there *nowt* I've never had?'

'Aye!' says Grandma. 'Whalebone soup!'

The scarf tore in the kitchen. Blue. It was a game until it tore, snatching it off Aunty Kitty's neck while they had dinner. 'He goes too far!' Grandma said, and Aunty Kitty held it up – 'It's done for!'

Blue. The noise of tearing. Darkness comes out of it. Grains. Turning me to stone. Aunty Kitty puts the scarf down by her bowl. Grandma lifts her spoon. 'Ignore him!' Mam says.

I have to fight it off.

...don't you know I can sew it? Don't you know? I've some blue cotton. I can sew it. Don't you know? I can. I can, can't I? Don't you know?

Soup just goes on dripping off the spoons. Grains of darkness coming. They're winning, aren't they? They're winning. I'm surrounded.

2

The grass is long. I can't go.

'Go on!' Mam says. 'He's an American. They're nice. Say, *Have you got a stick of gum, chum,* and he'll give you some chocolate.'

Why will he give me chocolate if I ask for gum?

Anyway, the grass is long. He smiles at me, leaning over the wall, while Mam plants flowers on her dad's grave. 'Go on!' she says. I can't. The grass is long.

∾

Morning. A bright day in our backyard. Everybody out enjoying sunlight. Then, *LOOK!* Flashes of tracer in the sky: a Messerschmidt 109 fleeing towards the sea, a Spitfire wheels to chase, wing near touching our rooftops...No, a Hurricane, says Uncle Hugh, and he knows best. He's taken the test. It's one of ours.

'Be off!' Grandma shouts, shaking her fist at the sky. 'Be off wi' you! Let honest folk alone!'

The mothers are all cheering in the backyards, and I watch the long wisps of white smoke slowly dying against the blue.

Cousin Eric clambers through the back fence in his gas mask. He's Donald Duck. That's a trick to fool the Germans. I've got Mickey Mouse. Grandma says they're in the flicks... *in the flicks*... What's flicks?

'It's flickers,' Eric says, 'like Charlie Chaplin.'

'Will I like the flickers, Grandma?'

'Aye, I daresay,' she says, 'though it's nobbut silliness.'

Back kitchen cold...

Snow falls, big flakes, out of the hazed dark. I've got the back door open to watch it build on the back step. 'Gives me rheumatics just to look at it!' Grandma says. Toc toc toc, I make the brown stool wobble. Flame hisses in the mantel. The garden hisses, crackling with snow. It goes on forever, too far to think about, on and on...toc toc toc toc toc...

Near and far...

Little thud of Uncle Hugh's bike down the passage. How do we know it's him? He's on his way. *Stamp stamp*

19

stamp around the water tank, boot on back step, legs go past . . .

'Roy . . .' he says. *Roy.* My name.

'Set thee by t'fire, Hugh!' Mam says. She speaks like that to Uncle Hugh. We all speak like that to Uncle Hugh. We speak like Grandma. Mam doesn't speak like that to me. And Grandma says, 'Not fit fer a dug!' Toc toc toc. I laugh. Not fit fer a dug.

'Eh, Hugh,' Aunty Kitty giggles, 'is it true you've put a stump o' candle in your bikelamp?'

Cheaper than a battery. Toc toc toc uneven on the kitchen flags. Clink of cups and teapot, cup of tea for Uncle Hugh, *I don't mind if I do,* ha ha . . .

Black grate, little fire . . .

'Are you sure you want to be out the'ere in't kitchen, love?' asks Aunty K, bending her nose towards me. Toc toc toc. I nod. She pulls the door, not shut, though, not *quite* shut.

'No need to pull t'bloomin' blind, anyroad,' says Mam. 'It's better than a blackout, this, isn't it?'

A plane, high up in the dark, throbs, throbs.

'That on's lost!' Uncle Hugh says. 'Heinkell one one one by t'sound on it!'

'Be 'ome!' says Grandma. Aunty Kitty listens with her eyes, swaying inside her arms. *Lost.* Looking for Liverpool docks. Snowflakes settle on my shoes. I'm thinking about matches, the matches that burn in Liverpool and the fire in Uncle Hugh's hands . . .

It's a long road to the marshes, and you have to put sommat in your stomach. (Mam says this, handing him something on a plate.) That's where he goes, Uncle Hugh, up Ralph's Wife's Lane, riding his bike to the guns. The rest of them scoot off when they see him coming with that stump of candle in his bikelamp, for he looks like a ghost, he rides that slow. They think it's Ralph's wife with her lantern, still looking for Ralph after a hundred years...

'You can come aht nah,' he shouts. 'It's only me wi' a stump o' candle in me bikelamp...'

His cousin burned to death. They were little. Right in front of his eyes. Her dress went in the fire, long dresses they wore back then, right in the fire. It was in the parlour. He caught hold of it and tried to squeeze the flames out of it, like wringing out the washing. But he couldn't save her.

And now he sits there, saying nowt, leaning his elbows on his knees, fire showing through his hands. And outside the snow... one one one forever...

Never do I have to go to bed.

That winter, milk bottles turned into stones on the doorstep. My birthday came. I'm five! I can run faster than anybody on earth, except Eric. He's the champion. I know a lot. I don't need to go to school. *Grandma, I don't need to go to school, do I Grandma...*

There's a big fight all afternoon, Shelley Roaders and Marshside Roaders. Eric is boss of the Marshside Roaders, but he's only got six in his regiment and one of them's got irons on his legs. He keeps running home to tell his mam the plans. Snow keeps falling, snow on snow... Uncle Hugh's up Ralph's Wife's Lane with the Home Guard. He can't come home till morning. He'll be snowed in at the guns.

Better than a blackout . . . They keep saying it, they all keep saying it.

I dreamed it was my birthday. My cousins came from Crossens, Eric, Glenys, Phyllis, John. They line up at the kitchen table in their best clothes. They looked like ghosts, they were that quiet. Not a word out of them. I'm scared. 'Mam!' I shout. 'They haven't any presents!' Then frozen, glassy balls come rolling out of their mouths, run down their frocks and go bouncing all over the floor – *words, presents . . .* I crawl under the table and pull the cloth down to hide, to make a den, but one of the glassy things comes rolling in under the cloth and my mam's inside it.

They've captured somebody . . . dragged him feet first down the alley to Shelley Road through the snow. Eric tried to chase them, breathing hard in panic, couldn't catch them. Aunty Mary went round to get their mothers.

'Quick!' Eric shouts. I see him from my bedroom window, beating his frozen gloves together. 'Quick, Mam! They're doin' sommat to him!'

The mothers come and go, come and go. They're lost. Their breath mingles together and rises. They shout names and wait. Nothing. Just snow and silence. I'm sad . . . even mothers can get lost . . .

Next day, Eric said they got him back with ten marbles. I was in bed by then. I never dared ask what they did to him.

∾

The seriousness of letters . . . polishing the specs, the scratching pen . . . letters to Dad, letters to Uncle John, letters to Uncle Dick. Nobody smiles then, nobody plays. They don't want bus tickets. I wait, awkwardly abandoned, clicking the little bell of my bus conductor outfit that nobody wants to hear. Then Grandma says, 'Just run dahn't road an' put these in t'box, there's a good lad!'

Lytham Road after dark: a long, straight road, mist breeding in the hedges; far off, a post box in a little pool of light . . . Somebody hasn't drawn the blind, or there's a hole in the blackout. Between here and there, there's only dark. But Eric says there might be slashers. They have razors and hide in doorways. When you run past, they slash. Nothing would do any good, he says, only a suit of armour if you could get hold of one. There's one in the museum in the Botanic Gardens . . . overcoats are useless!

That's only in big cities, Mam says, not here. There's nothing to be afraid of here. How does she know? They might come here on holiday.

A fever of running, feet lost . . . I'm threaded on darkness. I find the letter-box, my arm encircles it, I stuff the letters in and look back . . . *look back* . . . no holes in blackout curtains now, no light . . . and how does anybody ever find the way home?

Aunty Kitty singing – perhaps the first memory of a memory. And perhaps it really was in Crewe, like in the song. It was a station, and the trains were late – huge, dim halls; steam swirling and lingering; soldiers moving like smoke

in their big coats, always lighting cigarettes (red fingers
and no faces), and a porter in black silk sleeves sweeping up
and down, up and down... That's when I remember Aunty
Kitty –

> *O Mister Porter, what can I do*
> *I wanted to go to Birmingham*
> *And they've put me off at Crewe...*

and I wonder why she sings *that* song to cheer me up; it's
the saddest song I've ever heard.

But Aunty Kitty was at home with Grandma, sitting by
the fire knitting socks for soldiers: just me and Mam on the
platform, waiting for a train to go and see my dad.

...I wake, I wake again. Slowly the train jogs on, moving,
moving again. I see fires, spurts of flame around us, fires
thrown into the air, so beautiful... and here the soldiers hide
the little fires of their cigarettes inside their fists. Another
explosion, by our window! A soldier grabs the blackout
blind and pulls it down, dropping his cig and grinding it
out. They all do that, suddenly afraid. One crosses to our
seat and squirms in beside me. He smiles and says, 'Bend
over like this...' and covers us, Mam too, with his big coat.
I must have been asleep. But now the blinds are up again.
Mam still asleep, soldiers asleep, moonlight passing over
their faces. Then one gets up, sways, picks his way over
the muddled legs, sees my eyes open, bends down, touches
me, smiles... turned to stillness, I fall against Mam's coat:

the navy-blue one, loose and soft, wide pockets.

'Why can't we go?' she says, waking.

'Daren't move,' the soldier whispers. '...sparks might attract 'em...'

Then slow, slow, slow, our train begins to creep.

∾

'Pull the trigger,' Dad says. 'Go on!' He holds the rifle for me, cold against my cheek. His hut is shaped like a barrel. Outside, we've seen planes with their wings folded up, we've seen searchlights... 'Go on! Pull hard...' No matter how hard I try, it just won't budge.

'Not strong enough,' Mam says. 'Not yet.'

So he puts his finger over mine and pulls. The rifle clicks, just clicks. Where's the bullet? 'Can't put a bullet in,' Dad says. 'Get into trouble!'

So what's the use? Without a bullet, it doesn't alter anything.

∾

House full of clocks...grandfather clocks, grandmother clocks, others too, just clocks. Up and down we go, up the black stairs and round the corners, listening to the clocks...

'Couldn't you find a place without clocks?' Mam says.

Walks, every evening, walks with Dad ('He has to get to know you,' Mam says) – so we walk, walk to a castle on a hill, then down a lane to a cobblestone bridge, then we lean over and look into the water, always black, always swirling round the same stones.

'I can see your face!' Dad says. 'Look, in the water...'
But he's making it up.

∽

The back kitchen door was left open for him so there'd be a bit of light for him down the passage, when he came home on leave from Africa, my dad. Grandma set up a wail when she heard it: 'It's leave as does for 'em!' she said. 'Just like our Harry, blown to bits on hill sixty, right after he'd been on leave...Leave's aa' reet, but it's when they goo back!'

Mam frowns. 'No, Mother!' she says...*mother*...She never says *mother*. 'That was in the last war, in t'trenches ...It's not the same now.'

Uncle Harry's monocle wasn't blown up. After that, it was Grandad's monocle. Grandad wasn't blown up. He went from trench to trench carrying water on his donkeys, and he never got a scratch. 'It was t'war as did for 'im, just t'same!' Grandma insists. 'Traipsin' through t'mud wi' them damn donkeys...'

'Gentle creatures, Lizzie!' Grandad used to say.

'Gentle be damned!' Grandma said.

'That's nonsense, Mother!' Mam says. 'He lived for years after that, you know he did...It was pneumonia on them building sites...'

'He's gone, that's all I know!' Grandma says.

And now the monocle's in the sewing-machine drawer with all the buttons. It's waiting there for an eye. I've tied a ribbon to it, so it's mine.

∽

Aunty Kitty sighs over her knitting. She creeps up on the grate, does Aunty K. She likes the fire. Grandma shakes out her specs, rocks in her rocker, flops her book open. Mam hangs on the mantelpiece and stares down into the fire. She's lost in thought. I heard Aunty Mary say that once, *lost in thought*, and I wonder about the lostness and the thought, and now I understand, I see it's the firelight where the thought gets lost, lost in the flickering. I'm scared she'll not find her way back...

Waiting... the ticking clock, the sudden spurt of brightness from the dying fire... Mam kicks the coal, lightens our darkness now and then...

What worries me is what am I going to say.

'Don't say nowt till you're sure it's him,' Eric says. 'Then ask if he had a nice journey.'

But that's not it, the right thing, I wish somebody would tell me what it is. I'm waiting under Grandma's rocker, watching the crack of blackness at the door.

Nobody else sees the air-force cap come through the crack and wave up and down. Just a cap – a blue cap with a badge, waving up and down. No hand, not even fingers. I watch it, think about it, wonder what to say. It's just a cap – nothing special about a cap. How long will it go on if I say nothing? Will it go away?

It's my dad, I suppose, outside. Nobody knows but me.

'Mam!' I say. 'I think somebody wants to come in...'

Then... dizzy... flung up into the air...

∾

'...how's he been?' Dad says, *dad*...His fingers always rolling cigarettes, his bony elbows sticking through his khaki jumper.

'Fretting...' Mam says. 'You know.' She gives him a knowing look, quick, then down again into the fire, kicking the flames to make the coal fall...

They stand like that, not looking at each other, one at each end of the mantelpiece as though nothing's changed. *What's missing now?*

Dad's home. Dad's home from the war. But I don't understand.

Next morning I see him in bed and creep down into the cold kitchen. There's a train set laid out on the floor, wasn't there last night. I sit in Grandma's rocker and watch it from a distance, wondering whose it is.

∾

His cig lighter's made from a bullet – but it doesn't float – no good as a destroyer, sinks in the water tank, falls through the glaze of dust. Dad rolls his sleeves up, can't reach far enough – *It's a gonner!*

...rolls sleeves down again, asks Grandma for a match...facing the setting sun in our back yard...*Let's watch the sun go down*...

Over the water tank, horse flies zoom in with torpedoes...

'Getting damp...' Dad says. 'Coming in?' He flicks his fag end into the water. I bang my fist against the water tank – BOOM – dust breaks in fragments...BOOM...darkness, don't know what to say...

'Coming in?'

I think I'm going to cry.

Then he carries me to bed on his shoulders. On the landing he sings, *Goodnight Mister Moon*...and after he pretends to be a ghost on the stairs.

'DON'T!' I shout...not on the *stairs!*

∾

When Dad came home from the war, he emptied his kitbag in the kitchen. Right at the bottom, he found it. Black as a slug, it was!

'It's a banana!' he said. 'It was yellow in Alexandria...'

I took it upstairs on a tray, a banana on a plate with a knife and fork. Usually, I took a cup of tea. That was my job, waking Grandma in time for chapel, drawing her curtains. I plonked the tray down on the bed – 'BREAKFAST...'

Aunty K sat up and leaned forward. Grandma struggled up out of the depths of her feather bed, feeling for her specs. 'What is it, Kitty?' she says.

Aunty K screws up her eyes and shakes her head. No bloomin' idea!

'IT'S A BANANA!'

Silence. They don't believe me.

'Is it?' Grandma says. She looks worried about this. 'Are you sure?'

Aunty Kitty rubs her eyes and looks again: 'Bloomin' 'eck!' she says. 'It is an' all! A banana...a banana wi' a knife and fork!'

On Grandma's bedside table there's a Welsh Bible and Grandad's box. In the box there's a map of London Midland Northern Railroad, some pictures, and a copy of *The Last of the Mohicans*. She won't give it me because she likes old Hawkeye. On top of the dressing table there are two glass mountains – Grandad's jewels. He only worked one day at the glass factory, Grandma says: he couldn't abide the stench. He walked home with those jewels in his pockets. Eric says they're just lumps of glass. He's wrong. They must be jewels.

'Aye...' Aunty K says. 'They're jewels right enough! I do

believe they must be jewels! Me dad would never have carried 'em all t'way from Warrington if they weren't jewels!'

Walking into Grandma's bedroom is like walking into sleep, into a sea of sleep. But when Aunty Kitty wakes, she gives a little giggle – 'hoo hoo' she says – and that makes stepping-stones across the lino... 'hoo hoo.' I can walk on those.

∾

One day, Aunty Mary says: 'Can you guess what's happened, Roy... Can you guess? The war's over. That's nice, isn't it?'

'Did we win?' I say. 'Will we have lights in t'street?'

Just one gas lamp in our cul-de-sac, but one day a soldier came looking for his home, and nobody had ever seen him around here before the war. Even Mrs Henshaw, who'd lived in that house since she was a little girl, had never set eyes on him! 'You didn't live here, love. If you're a Rimmer, you should try Banks.' And tapping her head towards my mam, she whispered, 'Daft in th' head... that's what happens to 'em. Forgot where he lived!'

But he just kept walking up and down our cul-de-sac, and when it began to turn cold he went shinnin' up that lamp post and wrapped his arms around the glass to keep warm. All night he stayed there, sitting on the cross-bar like it was a horse. When he came down, he could hardly walk. Never saw him again.

'And we didn't even gie 'im a bit o' breakfast!' Grandma said.

∾

31

Dad got his job back. Sweet packer at Williams's. Has to get the train home every night. No life, Mam says. Nearly midnight when he comes home. I watch through the curtains, wait till he carries me to bed.

They go old-time dancing. Even Aunty Kitty goes.

'What do they do, Grandma?'

'Jump up and dahn like silly foo's!' she says, then settles herself in her chair. 'Pull t'chain, there's a good lad.'

'Can't reach, Grandma.'

'No peace!' she says. 'Dear me, Dick! No peace for t'wicked!' Her sigh fills the kitchen. She heaves herself up to turn the gas low. Flakes of white feather fall, but when I touch them there's nothing. She tosses some coal back on the fire, breaks it with Grandad's poker, leaning over till I'm scared she'll fall in, falls back into her chair at last. Then she does her hair, lets down the tight bun, stores the hairgrips in her pinnie pocket, combs down her hair that is straight and fine and silver. It used to be so long, she says, that she could sit on it. That was when she was young.

'How old were you when you married Grandad, Grandma?'

'None o' thy business!' she says...Then says, 'I were a lass of eighteen summers...an' I were such a rush our Dick were feart I'd slip dahn t'drain...'

Now she scrapes the stray hairs together, knots them into a bow on her palm, and blows it into the fire.

I rock in the rocker, rock rock rock, till the rocker hits the back wall and stops, then drag it up to the grate and start again, rock rock rock...every rock's a second, sixty seconds in a minute, sixty minutes in an hour...three hours in overtime-dancing...three times rocking the rocker till it bangs against the back wall...but I still can't keep Grandma awake.

She has dreams, that's the trouble. She falls asleep with the comb in her lap, the book open, her breath whistles between her teeth, she sighs and mumbles, and I know she's gone somewhere else, somewhere without me. I come off the rocker then. I study her face, I know it better than my own. I study her hands – the finger with the wedding ring grown deep into the flesh. Sometimes I pick her pocket, look in her purse: always one penny with a hole through it, a Queen Victoria penny, the one her dad made for her to wear like a necklace. It's a lucky penny!

She stirs in her sleep. 'Dick! Dick...' she shouts. 'Wheere a' t'a'?'

I'm scared. I don't want her to go off like that, leaving me alone. I know she runs off up Ralph's Wife's Lane in her sleep. She's eighteen then. She sees the wives waiting on the sea bank, singing their hymn, and the horse galloping wildly back over the marsh...only the horse...

'HELLO GRANDMA!'

'What's up?' she says, struggling out of the chair. 'What's up?'

'It's only me...'

She flops back. I know she's disappointed. 'Just chilt...' she says. Not Grandad. Then she sits bolt upright, face of stone, sings *Crimond*...that's enough to make the sea hold its breath.

∾

Beauty used to fly half-way around the kitchen with one wing. That's because the cat pulled the other wing off, right through the cage . . . that was the cat who jumped into Aunty Kitty's soup then disappeared forever. Out through the back door, never came back.

'Good riddance!' Grandma said. That happened before I was born, but I can still see it.

She used to say, *Good morning Kitty, put the kettle on* before cat got her wing. Afterwards, she never said a word. One day we buried her under an elderberry bush in a chocolate box, an oval chocolate box with a picture of blue mountains on the lid. Mam had been keeping it for something special. Her tail feathers stuck out, still yellow, but sad.

Then Pete, my little Welsh terrier, buried in a shoe box with his hind legs sticking out. Some boys threw stones at him, and then he died. We buried him under the elderberries. Dad prayed. *Thank you, Lord, for our little dog, Pete* . . . I wish he'd prayed for those boys, for Jesus to throw stones at them. Prayers were like that – always wrong.

I didn't cry for Beauty. I didn't even cry for Pete. But later on I crept under the hedge and cried in secret – just for the bits left hanging out. It was dreadful to bury them like that. I cried because we never had the right boxes.

∾

I did think Grandma was crying once.

The preacher was a tub-thumper, and Grandma could never abide a tub-thumper. She got up half way through the sermon, tossed her money on the plate. 'I didn't come here to be damned by thee!' she said, then she grabbed me by the sleeve and off we went. She sat down in the porch to get her breath. That's when I thought she was crying. The air around her turned black. But then I knew, I knew – she wasn't crying. She was having a giggling fit!

'I ne'er cried but twice,' she said. 'Once for our Dick and once for th' owd dug.' She died, once, too. She ran down to Jordan and saw her sister Sarah on the other side. 'Come on, Lizzie!' Sarah shouted. 'It's grand over here!'

'But I've our Peg to look after,' Grandma said – I can't come yet...' The Lord was on the Great White Throne. 'All right, Lizzie!' He said, and she came back.

Grandma laughs till she's fit to bust. She says: 'We laughed from t'day we were wed til t'day afore he deed...' When she sneezes, the dishes rattle in the kitchen and the piano booms. Same when you kick it.

One day I told her I was going to marry Ann Parks when I grew up, and she laughed till she could hardly stand, then started sneezing in her apron. But it wasn't funny.

Ann Parks has long, black hair, and she'll be a lass of eighteen summers...

One day it isn't right. The room isn't right, and I'm not sure that I'm the same me. I have to go to school. I can't get up. I slide out of bed and crawl to the top of the stairs...the whole house is turning a slow somersault...I'm wet...I've been in the jungle, I've fallen in the river...I shouldn't have thought about the jungle.

Mam can't do it. She sticks the medicine up my bum and

it flies out again. Doctor Lyle did it easy. 'I can't do it!' Mam says, and she starts crying. Grandma shouts. Aunty K and Aunty Mary are crying on the landing. *Can't do it! Can't do it!*

'Can't do it!' Grandma says. 'Can't do it! What's that supposed to mean, *can't*? Tha MUN do it...D'you want to lose him?'

That's torn it! Aunty K and Aunty Mary start wailing. I can hear them far off, like in another ocean. I don't care. I wish they'd shut up. *'Mam says we're going to lose him...'*

I'm too tired...I know what's happening, I understand. *Lose him.* They think I'm going to die. We lost the parrot and we lost the budgie and we even lost my little dog. Now we'll lose me. It doesn't matter. I don't mind being lost. I try to say, *'I don't mind...'* but nothing comes, nothing at all, no words. Then I remember we didn't lose the cat. The cat got lost after she jumped into Aunty Kitty's soup. The cat got lost, we didn't lose her...not our fault...she just went off and never came back...she got lost...

Islands...each sound makes an island, each noise... noises downstairs, Mam, Grandma, Aunty K...noises outside...sounds swell in me. Jagged sounds make jagged islands, smooth sounds make globes, puddles...every sound makes something, no matter how tiny it is, no matter how minuscule...some islands are smaller than pinheads, others bigger than anything I know, big, big as the universe where I live at 213 Lytham Road, too big to hold, and between all these sounds is the rocking hiss of the gaslight...

Then Dad. He comes round the door, holding something in front of him. He slides into the room, sits on the edge of the bed, puts something into my hand and wraps my fingers round it: a catapult.

'It's for shooting paper pellets... OK? Only for paper...'

I nod. Just for paper. It's made of plaited wire and bunches of elastic bands, black sticky tape around it to make a handle. He helps me to sit up and make a pellet, folding the paper over and over, folding and folding... so much folding! Then his fingers enclose mine, we pull the elastic... pellet hits the wall... 'It's fun, isn't it...' he says. 'It's fun. OK?' I nod. 'Only for paper. Promise?' I nod.

Alone, I see how the wires are twisted, how they bend painfully, criss-crossing each other, how the black tape hides the points of pain, how the bunches of elastic are struggling to untie themselves... I'm glad I'm not a catapult... I try to put a pellet into the catapult by myself, I try to pull... no use!

Who wants a catapult?

...the big thing and the little thing... this is everything... this is all that matters... big thing little thing... up and down... growing bigger going smaller... I have to hold them... can't hold... everything goes big, my arm, the bed, the room up here at this end where my head is, then little down there where my feet are, falling down towards darkness... I can't help it. What did I do wrong?... I can't help it, I can't hold...

'Mam! I can't hold it...' I have to grasp them and hold, the big thing that swells up and up and the little thing that shrinks and shrinks, smaller than anyone could grasp, fleeing from between my fingers...

... delirious... whispers and whispers...

... can't hold it... don't want to go down there again, the

dark down there, where I don't know where I am...lost in darkness...

Then, when everything goes quiet down there, like under black water, I just don't want to come up again...but have to feel that swinging bed going up again, so I begin to slip off this bed, this world, life, slip and slide, grabbing at things as they pass...*Stop it, Mam, stop it...make it stop!*

...at last, the bedroom comes back...I look at it, calm, quiet. I don't know where I've been.

∾

Mother lights the candle: I see through. Her fingernails make rosy windows, and the candlelight dances over their faces, Mam, Dad, Grandma, Aunty Kitty. The magic lights the wallpaper, flickering. Mam looks at Dad, a glance: *Is it all right?* He glances back: *Yes, it's all right...*

...got to find sommat to amuse him...

It's a magic lantern, that's what Dad says. Got it for ten-and-six...*a magic lantern for ten-and-six*...anything magic for ten-and-six...anything *magic*...

Somebody's coming up the stairs...door opens...*'Any room in the gods?'* It's Aunty Mary and Eric...even Uncle Hugh. They all traipse in and sit on my bed. And I know why: I'm not dying any more...I'm still here...I'm going to watch the show!

Clean sheets all over me, sheets like the sky. I feel as though I'm spreading out forever. Then I remember something very strange: *Dad made a catapult!*

'Come into the garden Maud...' says Grandma. I slide out into the back yard. *I'm Outside!* Grandma's sharpening the breadknife on the step. Some birds are singing in the elder-berries. Everything that's the same as it was before has changed completely. I never saw it like this before. I never knew what it was like. *Shake hands*, Dad says sometimes. *Be friends!* Now, I want to shake hands with every leaf. I want friends everywhere.

...move very slowly down the entry into the front garden. The grass is longer. Girls are playing jacks on the pavement. Their chattering and giggling fills the cul-de-sac. They can't see me. Our hedges are thick, very thick and high and green. I lie in the grass and crawl under the hedge. The girls are squatting cross-legged on the other side. If leaves don't get in the way, *I see...*

...blue, brown, white, and even green. Green's best, I think.

The gatepost is covered in green mould. I can scratch my secrets on it. One for green, two for brown, three for white, four for blue. It's the Bible of colours...It's like Joseph. If I *see*, I scratch another on the gatepost.

Then Mam comes back from her insurance round, wheels her bike through the gate, looks at my scratches, smiles...I breathe quick with shame: *how did she know?*

It's windy, there by the chimney. I didn't think of that. I dragged the parachute out of the cupboard, bit by bit, stuffed one end out of the little window over the front porch, and climbed out after it. But the other end was still in the cupboard. *Still in the cupboard ... How big's a parachute?* How can I parachute off the roof if half of the parachute is still inside the cupboard? I can't, can I?

Raymond watches me, standing by our front gate with his arms winding between the palings. He's smiling. He knows I can't do it. I climb higher, so I can touch the chimney pots. I can see Blackpool Tower and the sewage works on the marshes. What next? I'm scared ...

Then Grandma appears in her pinnie with her arms folded and the breadknife sticking up in her fist.

'O parachutes is it?' she says. 'Well, tha' can parachute back through that window this minute ...'

I'm in luck ...

Mam comes home, cuts the parachute in half and sends me to bed. From the window, I watch Raymond skating up and down the cul-de-sac on his big trike called ACE. He's a genius on that trike.

'Can't be a genius,' Eric says. 'A genius knows everything, and *he* doesn't know how to talk.'

It's a secret. He *does* know, just doesn't want to. I have to whisper to myself when I talk about Raymond, or Eric gets jealous. That's because of the day we took him to Sunday school so the Superintendent, Mr Hargreaves, could pray over him. But he held onto him by his ear, so Raymond lashed him a good kick in the shin and just ran ... out of the chapel and into the street, and Eric couldn't catch him HAHAHA ... Couldn't catch him, the little imp! Nobody tried *that* trick again!

And when the lads from the Ferry, the ones with steel

swords, the ones who threw stones at little Pete, those lads... when they told him to pull his pants down so they could throw stones at his bum, he just went into a fit, a fit like a dog run over...

'We didn't touch him,' their chief shouted. 'We never touched him...' and they ran off, half scared to death!

That's why Raymond is a genius, whether he can talk or not.

Sometimes the parson comes to dinner. Two things I don't like about Sunday dinner. One is the signature tune on the wireless – *Confidentially*... that's how it starts, and then it goes on, five times the same word, horrid word, makes me squirm. The other is the dreadful thing somebody says just when we're about to start eating, after saying grace. It's always the same, hotpot or anything else, the same dreadful thing: *Dig deep, parson, there's plenty o' meat in t'middle!*

No sooner is the food on the plate, than somebody has to say this. Not too bad if it's Grandma. She gets it over with. But Dad's the worst – he never says the whole thing, but just *Dig deep, parson*... Then there's a wait. Aunty Kitty starts to giggle. She knows what's coming. Then Mam says, *O aye...Dig deep, parson...HA HA...*Then WE WAIT AND WAIT... until at long last, sometime, sometime, SOMEBODY says it...

THERE'S PLENTY O' MEAT IN T'MIDDLE!

May the Lord make us truly thankful! Then we can start!

On Sunday afternoons, Bill comes to call on Aunty Kitty. He's her boss in the Civil Service. He comes to the front door and sings:

Will ye gang tae the heilands Lizzie Lindsey,
Will ye gang tae the heilands wi me?
Will ye gang tae the heilands Lizzie Lindsey,
My bride and my darling tae be?

Aunty Kitty giggles and says, 'Here's my *beau*...'

'Aye, and drunk as usual,' Grandma says.

'He isn't drunk at all. He only has a pale ale. That's trouble with my mam, you can't be cheerful but what she says you're drunk!'

Bill comes from Glasgow. He's a Fraser. They were wiped out at Culloden, all but one or two...

'*He* had the good fortune to escape!' says Aunty Kitty... HA HA!

But Bill looks dour... 'Not a laughing matter, Kitty!' he says.

Well, sometimes he can laugh as daft as owt!

When they've gone, I have the front room to myself. I play quietly until evening service, first piano practice, then my secret game. *Not* chess. I use the white girl pawns and the black girl pawns, the castles and the queens. I'm a knight, sometimes white sometimes black. I don't believe in kings or bishops.

On the wall, Grandma's favourite picture hangs – *Ruth Gleaning in the Fields of Boaz*. Ruth kneels in the middle of a field with Naomi standing behind her. Boaz stands in front looking down on Ruth... looking *down*! He's 'casting a favourable eye on Ruth'. So that's a favourable eye. So now I understand what *that* means! Standing over her, looking down... and her dress... no wonder he's...

TAXI...

I'm just in time to see Dad and Uncle Bill carrying Aunty Kitty in through the front door.

'Dear God!' Grandma wails. 'What have you done to her?'

'She's all right!' Dad says. 'She's all right...'

Well, all right? She'd gone to pieces, arms and legs in the wrong places, and streams of water running down her nose and her fingers like Jack Frost. Bill had rocked the rowing boat again...but too much this time. She had fallen out head first, and stuck head down in the mud...

'...thinking about our Roy...couldn't stop thinking about our Roy...'

Me? Why me? I should understand that, shouldn't I?

Aunty Kitty soon got better. It was Uncle Dick who died. Grandma suddenly dropped down into her chair: 'He's gone!' she said. She didn't cry. Her face turned to stone and her eyes were pale and clear. 'How do you know, Grandma?'

'I alus know. I feel 'em slip away...'

I think of the last time I saw him and played the piano for him. He'd run away in his pyjamas and hitchhiked to Marshside. He wanted to live in our front room. But he had TB. The house had to be fumigated, and the police came to drive him back. Dad took the last picture – Uncle Dick and Aunty Kitty together on the front lawn.

'Come on, Dick,' she said. 'Let's show 'em we still know how to laugh...' Then the police car came.

∞

I dreamed about the way to school. It was at the beginning of the world. Everything was fresh and beautiful and empty. The street was like something from the middle of the sea. I was the only living thing. I was happy.

I looked across the churchyard over the wall, over there, that's the field where we have the Rose Queen Festival. Nothing there now, except a bull, wandering lazily in the grass, tossing, nodding his head slowly, dragging his hooves, step by step, going nowhere.

Then I see a girl crossing the field, carrying a satchel. She hasn't noticed the bull. She walks with her head down, sadly. 'It's not safe!' I shout. 'Watch out, watch out, there's a bull!' She starts to run, but not quick enough, no, nothing like quick enough. I have to save her, I have to scare the bull.

I throw myself over the wall and run, furiously, screaming hard as I can, I must get between the girl and the bull to scare him off. 'Get over the wall,' I shout. 'Quick, quick!' O she tries, but she's not quick enough, she's too late, she falls, the satchel spills out its things into the grass... What can I do? I'm trying my best to reach her, but the bull moves faster, I'm helpless, the scream in my head is a fever going higher and higher... I can't see... I can feel, though, grass and thistles whipping my calves... I run on in blindness.

Then stillness. I can see again. Everything has changed colour. The grass is red and golden, the grass-seed and flower petals fly up in the air, and they have turned into jewels, sapphires, emeralds... I know what these words mean now, sapphires, emeralds... It's more beautiful than anything I've ever seen, and I think *I knew it should have been like this*. But where's the girl? She's getting up, gathering her things to put in her satchel. Can you see the colours? I shout. But she runs from me. She's terrified. Why? What's the matter?

Come back!... She dashes off. The colours scatter into the air around her legs like fireworks. And then I see...I see what the matter is. When everything changed colour in the darkness, I turned into the bull, and when I look down, I see the hooves, bull's hooves, scraping through the grass, sending the colours up into the air, so beautiful. But I'm the bull now, and there's nothing I can do about it.

3

We're on the train to Liverpool.

'Don't you remember?' Mam asks. I shake my head.

'Don't remember Granny dangling you on her knee?' Shake my head.

'Don't remember playing hide-and-seek with Grandad – that's your *dad's* father – and finding half-a-crown in the teapot?' Shake my head. I don't remember.

Yes I do – I remember trolley wires in the sunlight, coming out of a mist, remember dock cranes sticking up into the evening sky, remember searchlights sweeping the night, back and forth, back and forth. That's all I remember.

Dad hides behind the hedge.

'Push!' he says. 'Go on! It's only Grandad!'

Why should I be the one to push this little brass doorbell? Why doesn't Dad push it himself? It's very stiff and it hardly makes a sound. Nobody would even notice. We'd might as well go home.

'Ring again!' Dad hisses. 'Push harder...'

But I don't need. The door is opening. I can see some thick, brown pants, and hands like chestnut leaves. A pair of spectacles flap to and fro between those huge fingers.

'*Who* is ringing *my* doorbell?' says the voice. Those great big fingers hook the spectacles around his ears. 'And who is this standing at my door...What is your name?'

I would like to run away, but Mam and Dad are hiding, so I have to say it: *Roy Watkins is my name...*

...I saw the stairs coming at me, then my head smashed the lampshade.

'Put him down, you're scaring him to death...' Yes, now I remember. That's Granny. Now I remember Granny.

Then I drop. Suddenly I'm lying on soft carpet looking up into blue eyes. I could lie here forever. 'Scared?' the voice says. 'Better not be...not if he's a Watkins...'

Dad says, *Hello Dad...* That's funny, Dad says...But there's something wrong. I hide it inside. I know more than what's good for me, that's the trouble. I can hear it in Dad's voice, something I shouldn't know: *My dad doesn't like his dad...*

∾

Mam and Dad go shopping. Grandad warms his backside by the fire. Granny scoots here and there in and out of the scullery. I sit at the kitchen table eating cake.

They have a secret language, Grandad and Granny. It's soft like sighs, like shushing and hushing. It's Welsh.

Granny says: 'Where Grandad comes from there are two mountains, one called big and one called little. And the funny thing is, the one called little is really very big. It's only two or three inches smaller than the one called big!' She laughs, throws up her hands.

I've never seen a mountain, so I keep on eating cake.

'The child isn't interested in that old stuff!' says Grandad.

'Of course he is!' says Granny. 'Of course he is...' And suddenly she yanks the scullery door open and points inside. There's one shelf of tins and another of books.

'That's a funny place to keep books, isn't it?' she says. 'And d'you know why I keep books in my scullery? It's just because Grandad hasn't made me a bookcase yet, and he's a carpenter, a very good carpenter, too.'

Then Granny catches my hands between hers and looks me in the eyes: 'Your grandad once earned sixteen guineas in a week! Just think... sixteen golden guineas in a week! Never forget that, Roy...'

I have a memory. Dad sat on Granny's lap and promised to buy her a silk dress. She'd always wanted one.

Then Grandad came home four sheets to the wind. He was a policeman. His cape was back to front, he'd lost his helmet. A neighbour woman reported him. Four years off the bottle. Best four years of her life. Then he met Bobby Bach, an old companion from Wales. Little Bob. He came home four sheets to the wind. He was done for.

Granny never got a silk dress.

∞

I dreamed about a book. Somebody gave it me. It had all the answers. I wrapped my arms around it, but when I

47

woke up it had gone. It wasn't just a dream, it was a real book, one of the books in Granny's scullery. One she's going to give me when I'm older. Latin, French, and music. That's why we have to go to Liverpool. I must remember: in Liverpool it's *Granny*, not Grandma.

Sheets, greenish in the dark light. Downstairs, down the ladder under the skylight, my uncles are in the front room, Uncle Jack and Uncle Stan. There's a vase of flowers between them on the sideboard, and in the flowers there's a bottle of whisky.

Up here, in the bed, there's Granny.

'Where's Grandad?'

'Hush!' Mam says.

There are so many people here around the bed, people I don't know, I get left out, pushed to the back. I don't like their coats or their whispers. Then a voice says: 'Where's Bob's child?' I'm shoved up to the front. 'She wants you ... You have to say something ...'

There's a crumpled sheet, not white, not very white, and Granny's thin hand. I see her. Nothing but thinness. But I say nothing ... I'm saying *nowt!*

I hide behind the curtains, and when they've all gone down the ladder I come out. Now I can talk.

'Hello, Granny!' I say, breathless on the threadbare carpet. 'I can talk now.'

She's asleep, and I can watch her face. I can wait till she wakes up. Then Mam's face appears at the top of the ladder. 'Come on down,' she says.

'But I can talk now, Mam ...'

'Come down. She can't hear you any more.'

We're going to see a mountain. It's another country, Aunty Mary says. *Yorkshire . . .*

'Well,' Dad says, 'not so much a mountain as a moor . . . but it is like a mountain . . . lakes and valleys and crags.'

Crags . . . I like the sound of crags. And there's a castle on the crags, because it's called *Hardcastle Crags*.

'No,' Dad says, 'the crags are the castle . . . It's just a name, that's all . . .'

We have to go first, Mam, Dad and me. We have to light the fire. But first we have to find the cottage, and to find the cottage we first have to find the path of a hundred steps. It's through a hole in a wall. Dad nods. That's the very first. We have to find the hole through the wall.

'Watch out for holes,' he says as the bus lumbers up and down the hills. 'Watch carefully, we don't want to miss it!'

'Midge Hole!' the bus conductor says. 'That's what you want, Midge Hole, bottom of the steps.' He makes the bus stop, and there's the hole. It's a little iron gate through a stone wall.

We plunge into a gloom of leaves.

. . . down, down, one hundred steps into a valley, I skip . . . I don't care if things know I'm coming . . . *they're all mine!*

Suddenly we're out on a path again, walking on pine needles, and here's a cobbled yard, a stone wall, a steep hillside overgrown with ferns. Clouds skip over, blotting the bright green with shadow . . . and I see it all . . . a row of low cottages cut deep into the hillside. It takes my breath away.

'*Dad, look!...It's just like it's supposed to be...*'

I feel tears welling-up...This is new! I've never been here before.

∾

A picture! Dad's brought his Brownie box camera. It's been all over Africa! He's decided to take pictures. He keeps saying: 'It's a matter of composition...'

Matter of composition...sacred words.

'...down further...down in the bare patch...over there.' I wade neck high in a jungle of blinding green until I find the little patch of withered brown – *There!* Dad shouts. *Freeze!*

Sunlight blooms and fades. The sun's important. My fingers want to fidget, but I can stop them. What about everything else? What about the swaying ferns, the new ferns curled tightly, little heads wound tight as Mam's green bobbins, what about butterflies? We need God to stop everything while Dad takes the picture. Then, like winding up the gramophone, it can all start again at the beginning. Then sun comes, trying to make me blink.

'*Hold it...*'

At long last, God takes the needle off. *Stillness!*

'OK...'

I breathe again. The ferns may uncurl.

∾

The moment comes. Grandma sets foot into the valley. Came with Eric and Aunty Mary in a charabang. I see her toss her head, set foot into the valley in her new shoes. I run to meet her. She'll say: *'Vanity! Nowt but vanity! Folk should stay home and be happy.'* I know she'll say it.

And I'll laugh.

∾

Rain, rain on the leaves, we're in a ring of leaves, we're in a den.

All day I search...cupboards, corners, under stairs ...backs of shelves...cubbyholes...There has to be something I don't know, some thought, some secret...

And all the time the rain roars even louder than the river...through me, through everything, falling...

I put my head down on one of the stairs going up to the bedroom, and I listen to the sounds inside the wood... I hear rain...

Grandma tells tales. She tells about the girls who sat outside with spinning wheels. Outside this very door. They sat there spinning. Darkness fell, and they sat there spinning ...'Grandma, tell me more stories. Same story...'

All night the stream roars in the valley over its stones. I hear it in my sleep. It runs through me, dark and anxious. I long for something in this roaring water. I think it's happiness.

And then the eyes of squirrels in the leaves...a red squirrel on the cobbles by our door...

'There!' Grandma says. 'You've seen one, my mind's at rest...'

So dark comes through the trees. What do I want when I feel spread around the walls?

There's a pike in the mill dam. It's famous, Eric says. It can bite your arm off.

Mam tucks her hair under the blue rubber swimming cap and lowers herself slowly into the dam. The water runs out over the stones, slides down the dam, dragging long strands of weed, green slime, like hair.

I'm scared.

Dad laughs. 'She's a good swimmer, your mam. Didn't you know?'

It's deep. There's a pike. 'O aye!' Dad says. 'They're scared of humans, don't worry...' *Don't worry!* They should listen to Grandma. She says it's plain foolishness, swimming. That's what it is... That's what it is... *It's plain foolishness!*

'I'll have to come out,' Mam says. 'He's scared stiff!'

At last we meet Grandma at the mill for tea. We meet them in the cobbled yard, Grandma, Aunty Mary and Eric.

Today the lunatics have come from the asylum, all shapes and sizes. Big heads and funny, gawping faces. They surround me, cooing, stretching out their hands towards me...

'Don't be scared,' Dad says. 'They like children. Ignore them.'

I'm trying to ignore them, but their fingers are a nuisance. They keep going everywhere, poking and pushing, pulling at buttons...

'SCOOT!' Grandma shouts. 'SCOOT! SHOO!' She shakes her arms, and off they go. Then Grandma puts her arm around me and we march off together.

Time for tea.

Something happened here. This very room. The looms were smashed. The looms...*looms*...Today there are cake stands and little tables. I can't see the looms. But they were smashed. This very mill. And then they marched to Manchester, lads and lassies, and they were shot.

'Many a year ago...' Dad says.

Grandma stamps her foot. '*Many a year! Many a year!* What's that supposed to mean? It were wickedness...'

Many a year, and they were shot...Many a year, they were shot...

Just lads and lassies.

It was their water running over the weirs, and they never came home. Do the weirs remember? All that green hair running over the stones, is it theirs?

'It were a wickedness, whether it were many a year or no!' says Grandma, and she's ready for a fight. But then Eric pipes up: 'Hey, shurrup you lot! There's cream cakes!'

✎

We walk over the moors. I'm thirsty. Dad finds a stream of pure water, and I drink out of his hands.

I remember the stones, the water parting for them.

At last we get there. There was an old parson who used to shoot his gun over the graveyard. We see doll's books in tiny writing, dresses, some rifles that Dad calls *fowling pieces*. They were called the Brontës. This one and that one. Sisters in a little room.

'They must be very wicked people!' I say. That's because my Dad thinks all guns are wicked.

Walking back, we have to cross the river on stepping-stones. Dad gives me the Brownie box camera, shows me how to shield the little window from the sunlight so I can take a picture of them on the stones, Mam and Dad.

I drop the camera in the water, run over the stepping-stones: 'Let me in! I'm part of this!'

∾

The path to Midge Hole slopes into the gloom. It's nearly dark. We have to visit the Girl Guides. I'll go, if I can take my eye-of-fire ...

We have to tell a story, *where we were happiest* ... After the songs, after *One Man Went to Mow, One Green Bottle* ... After all that, we have to tell a story.

It's nearly dark. The girls hug their knees ... the camp-fire dies. Mam says she was happiest playing golf with her dad. They used to sneak onto the course after dark, when everyone else had gone home. They couldn't afford to join the club. They had a driver, a putter, and a four iron. Grandad smoked his pipe, and when he whacked the ball, sparks flew up and the white ball flew off down the fairway into the dark. That was her story.

Fire tells its story and the dark is winning. I've got my spark, my eye-of-fire. I shout, *'I'm happiest here!'*

Girls' laughter in the dark ... lost among leaves ...

'We don't want to do where we were saddest, do we?' Mam's nose wrinkles. 'Nooo ...' The girls don't want, don't want ... They shake themselves inside their skirts, hug their knees, make cradles of their arms...

I twirl my eye-of-fire and shout, *'I'm saddest here ...'*

∾

The beds creak. Old iron bedsteads. The stairs are steep. Grandma needs a shove. She says, 'These stones are bad for my back.'

All words are mystery. *Stones are bad for back . . .*

Then Aunty Mary giggles. 'You'll never guess,' she says. 'Guess who I've been thinking of . . .'

It's evening on the cobbles. We wait . . . 'Bispham Road Grandad!' she says. Then she claps her hands up over her head and buries her face in her apron. She can't speak for laughing. Mam just shakes her head: 'That house . . .' she says. 'It was too gloomy to contemplate!'

'Gloomy! I'll say! Gloomy . . . That were because he'd painted o'er t'winders.'

'Aye!' Mam says. 'Those great beasts everywhere . . . What d'you call 'em?'

'Buffalo,' Aunty Mary says. They all nod. Yes, buffalo. Grandma looks out across the valley, remembering something . . .

∾

Evening, we walk . . .

'. . . *hlthooroo eeooroo moroo lthblerooo mroo throo . . .*'

'What's all that?' Eric says.

'Welsh,' I say.

'Well, shurrup wi' it!' he says. 'It's driving me dotty!'

Evening slides in through the pines. We pass sandy places, pine-needle places, stony places . . . river moans on and on, talking to us.

'...*hlthroo woorubth*...*mloomloomloom*...'

'SHURRUP I SAID...'

After a while, I ask, 'Eric, what d'you know about buffalo?'

He's quiet for a while, then says, 'I know what you're thinking...' We reach the bridge, the place where Eric throws his stones. He squats on a boulder in midstream, darkness falling around us, and he begins to skim stones over the water. He watches every stone. He talks between. 'It were somebody,' he says, 'our grandad's grandad or somebody like that... He went off to America...'

Stone bounces over the talking current.

'On a wagon train...but his father was killed...his mother married somebody else, so he was sent home again...When he was old...'

Stone skips.

'...he painted all his house to look like America.'

Eric laughs. 'Aunty Kitty took him his dinner one day ...She had to go to t'lav, and when she looked up, there was an Indian wi' a tomahawk looking down on her...She ran home wetting her knickers...'

'Let's go!' I say.

'He's dead!' he says.

'We could find his house...'

Eric shakes his head slowly, skims a stone thoughtfully. 'I thought of that, too, but it's no good. They've knocked it down...'

'...*mloo hthlooroo bthgroo mroo hlth*......'

Almost dark on the stream, stone tips white in moonlight, and voices darker inside the water. Then, coming out of the pines, we see Grandma leaning over the wall, far up, far up the hillside, and lights, little yellow lights, tiny and far. Everything's all right here.

Look! Moon rising! Smoke from our fires!

∾

Home at two-thirteen Lytham Road I dream of a boulder with something under it. I wait, wondering what will come out of the dark. Then I make my way back through the pines along the river. I keep looking for the cottage. Night after night, I look for it. The dream goes on for years... No matter where I am, it goes on, and I wake from the night-long tumbling of the river...

∾

Piano...Came through the front door with a wedge of sunlight. Cost us ten-and-six and another five bob for carting it. Yellow wood, red silk, brass candlesticks.

'Antique, then?' said Aunty K.

'Aye, I daresay,' Dad said, 'but good condition, nowt broken. We'll get it modernised.'

It was all Grandad's fault. He wanted to play every instrument in the orchestra, and to do that he first had to make them, all of them! The only thing Grandma liked was the harp. She couldn't abide fiddles – all catgut and caterwauling – nor the stench of hide glue in her kitchen. He fitted out an orchestra and lent his instruments to folk from chapel so they could learn. After he died, the only one never returned was the harp, the beautiful harp that had taken all of a year to make!

It was Grandad who made music run in the family, and now I have to learn it.

Sometimes I think Grandad comes home to play the piano, and I hear him in the middle of the night. His music is the real music, the secret music. It's never on the radio. That's what I want to learn. But most, I want to make it up myself.

∾

Grandad made a lot of things. When I go on the bus with Grandma, she points to all the roofs he made and says: 'There's another that remembers him – but just t'same, it didn't make our fortune!'

I think, if roofs remember him, why not all the other things he made...the fiddle, the Bible-box, the breadknife?

Nothing made their fortune. But Grandad used to give his pay packet to the Sally Ann. They'd rattle their collection boxes at him in the street, and he'd give them everything. He couldn't resist. There was nothing left for Grandma. She had to walk to town and ask for her money back at the Citadel, and Tom Rimmer, boss at the Sally Ann, used to moan and mutter, 'Oh dear, Lizzie! Oh dear oh dear... What does he think you'll have to eat?'

Then she'd get the bus home, and they'd laugh!

∾

So it had come true – Mam had found a piano teacher, Miss Jones, half-a-crown the half hour.

'A Welsh woman!' Grandma said.

'O I don't know about that, I'm sure!' Mam said.

Grandma scowled and banged her stick on the lino. 'Jones is Jones and Jones is Welsh!' she said.

'Does she know the secrets?' I whispered. Aunty Mary heard me.

'O aye!' she said. 'She must know the secrets if she's a proper teacher.'

I stood there, where I'd been told to wait, on a carpet. Room full of little glass animals and ships – galleons made of sea-shells – piano, *grand* piano, not like mine.

Came on the bus. Grandma and Aunty Kitty have gone to the Kardomah Café while I have my lesson, and after I shall go there for a cream cake. Now I watch Miss Jones as she stands in the bow window watching the policemen arresting the man: 'They've got him, the bounder!' she says. Then they bash him against a wall, and when he falls over they kick him, kick him, kick him, then drag him to the black van, open the back doors, and throw him inside, head-over-heels like a sack of spuds. Miss Jones is banging on the window shouting, 'Encore! Encore!'

When I start crying, she grabs my hands and shakes them up and down. 'Oh don't cry! Don't cry!' she says. 'That man wanted old Hitler to win the war! You do understand, don't you? When you go home, you must say to your mother and father, *Local police have today arrested the last British hitlerite*... You can remember that, can't you? But don't mention the... you know.' She put her finger on her lips and went *Shhh*.

Then the lesson – lines and spaces, Middle C, and a five-finger exercise – CDEFG and GFEDC. When I play Middle C I should not be timid, I should make it *SING!* When *she* made it sing, the skin on her arm wobbled like a jelly.

'Did you learn owt?' Grandma asked. I was busy thinking, so I said nowt.

'Kitty, see if you can get sommat out of him...'

'I will, right enough,' said Aunty Kitty. 'It doesn't take much of a tickling, does it?'

And then she knelt down beside me on the rug.

'Come on, did you learn owt or did we waste our money?'

I whispered, 'Middle C.'

'Well, show us then...'

I crept to the piano on all fours, and felt along the keys. I stopped at Middle C and pressed down very slowly.

'What is it, Kitty? Is it right?'

'Aye, that's Middle C right enough...'

'Thank the Lord for small mercies,' Grandma said, and flopped back in her rocker.

Then Dad burst in: 'They've got him – you know, the loony, the Nazi – picked him up somewhere on Manchester Road!'

ॐ

I want sommat special. Perhaps I want some different clothes – that special coat with velvet collars, and the silk scarf that used to belong to Uncle Dick. When I ask Mam where they are, she pretends not to understand me: 'Don't be daft!' she says. Then she catches on. 'Goodness gracious me! It's that check coat with velveteen collars he's on about, the one he had when he was five... Eric had one matching and they got ruined when they walked round and round the Botanic in the rain! I chucked it out long since.'

'Oh dear!' she says. 'Well, it wouldn't fit you now, love!'

But WHY if I want it? WHY if it's the only thing I want?

There was something I wanted more – my baby brother – but Jesus wanted him in Heaven... That Jesus! He gets everything...

There was a message: I had to go to Aunty Mary's after school. 'Did you want a brother?' she says. 'Did you know? You have a brother. He's called Alan.'

I fly home like the wind. Dad's waiting for me with his bike ready to go.

'Come on!' he shouts. 'I'll take you on the cross-bar,

your mam will bring him to the window and you'll see him!'

Under the window, he gives his secret whistle...Suddenly, he points: 'Look! What did I tell you...See!' The curtain moves and there's my mam holding a white bundle. She pulls a lacy blanket away from the little face. For about half a tic...half a mo...I see him. Then she disappears.

'Supposed to be in bed...' Dad says. 'Still, you saw him, baby Alan, you saw your brother...'

On the way home in Rathmore Crescent, Dad pointed to a posh house. 'That's where you were born,' he said. 'Grandma's house. She bought it with your grandad's insurance, and then sold it when the war started because she thought Hitler wanted to blow it up!'

What's wrong?

It happens in dreams. I come home from school, sit down on the rag rug in front of the fire and stare into the flames. I see his face. Too late. The baby's gone. It was the midwife's fault, Aunty Mary says. Dad says, 'Let's talk to Jesus.' Grandma says, 'Leave her alone, there's a good lad! Don't pester her.' She throws things in the fire and blobs of flame drip. 'What's that?'

'Lairs to catch meddlers...'

My mam's upstairs, but I can't go. I come to the bottom of the stairs and look up. It's a steep cliff I can't climb. I keep slipping off the edge, losing my grip, falling. Mam's in the dark, crying.

*I should have had two, you know...It was the midwife's fault...
I should have had two. They struck her off, that woman...*

I didn't know a thing about it, of course, never regained con-sciousness... O mam. I saw his face... No love, no, no... you've imagined that.

∾

'My number's up!' Dad bellowed from the back door. 'A new house in Crossens – we've got one! New Crescent number 36.'

He'd been to the town hall to see the waiting list.

'Hurray!' Aunty Kitty shouted.

'Vanity!' muttered Grandma. 'Folk should stay put and be happy.'

'You'll be happy right enough when we've seen t'back o' them cockroaches!' Dad said.

'What, are there no cockroaches in Crossens?' Mam asked.

'No cockroaches when a house is built on sand,' Dad said. 'No cockroaches and no dry rot. Sand's best!'

...no more gaslight...switches for electric lightbulbs... lamp posts in the street all night...two lavs and a french winder, that's what Aunty Mary said...just think, *two lavs and a french winder*...and my own bedroom!

But outside by myself, I think of all things I might for-get. I loiter with the elderberries, think about the tree we brought from Hardcastle Crags, planted where we buried my little dog...I might forget...cracked dust on the water tank...better say sorry now...and the girls from the Valley, they'll stand at the window and watch us go.

They used to be there, didn't they? The girls, fair hair, black hair, happy, sad? Train that needed mending, aeroplane, Spitfire, Hurricane, one or the other. And my little friend, Raymond... *used to be*... a book that's gone forever...

In school, I'll sit all day thinking the strange words I must say to Miss Oswick... *We're moving house*... and then I'll hide out in the porch till everybody's gone, and I'll shut the gate behind me and turn left, left along Rufford Road, and I'll turn left again at the New Crescent and walk until I see the moving van outside number 36, and I'll see all our furniture in the road and Grandma sitting by herself in the middle of a pile of rubble in the garden with a scowl on her face and a cup of tea on her lap, and then I'll lie down in the road and laugh... I'll think that's the funniest thing I've ever seen, and I'll just laugh, I will... I'll laugh forever.

THE SECOND PART

36 New Crescent, Crossens

4

New world, all new. New houses built of pinkish brick with bright green doors and windows, all the same until people start painting them – ashamed to be council-house tenants, Dad says, because green's the corporation's colour. Pavement of big, sand-coloured flagstones, where girls can sit playing jacks. Our New Crescent is a single ring of houses, and a single road out onto Rufford Road. Behind the houses there's a broad dyke where fish sometimes float to the surface. Beyond the dyke, we can see for miles across Martin Mere.

From my window, I can see four streetlamps. Hardly a shadow between them. You could read a newspaper at midnight, Mam says. Dad comes out and sits on the front step. He nods towards the patch of earth in front – 'My lawn!' he says. 'Look!' And sure enough, tiny needles of grass are poking up all together. They weren't there yesterday! I walk up Rufford Road where the flags gleam blue, dark blue, I look at everything, telephone kiosks, greenhouses in the fields, lights in the library windows, and a strange feeling comes over me – I want to break something, I want to see something shatter, I want splinters to glitter under moonlight... *that* would be happiness.

One morning, Dad brought two rolls of wire netting home on his handlebars, bought from the war surplus warehouse. He built a bonfire behind the house, and tossed them in the fire to burn off the camouflage feathers. The sky filled with floating flames, and the stench of burning feathers lingered over us for days. We weren't the only ones to blame – that was the cheapest way to get a fence. But now – I tug Dad's sleeve – we need a dog!

Patch, a white, wiry-haired terrier pup with a brown patch over one eye, came home hidden under the lapels of Dad's raincoat. Dogs were not allowed on buses. His long life began badly, with an awful clout from Cousin Eric's cricket bat that sent him into hiding. We thought he was a gonner, but after a few days he came crawling on his belly up to the dining-room fireplace and lay there at peace, his favourite place for ever after. Grandma kept a jar of water on the mantelpiece to douse him when his tail caught fire. And from that spot, once every three or four weeks, he would suddenly stiffen and stand, slowly, with the hair over every bit of his little body standing up taut until he looked twice his usual size. Then, for about six or seven seconds, he would watch an invisible presence move slowly through the room from the side wall on his left to the door into the kitchen on his right, and only when that mysterious visitor had completely left the room, his size shrank and he dropped down again into a snooze. Dad was sure this came about because of the bang on the head, but Grandma was equally sure that he was watching a ghost ship – as our crescent was built on the reclaimed land of an ancient mere – and the dog's behaviour never changed in the least from one visitation to the next, nor did it ever occur anywhere else.

∾

I hear Grandma when she comes to bed – first hauling herself up the stairs, then my mam behind her pushing, new wood creaking every step. And then, *swish, swish* she goes, slewing her corsets first one way then the other.

'Ee Mam, I wish you wouldn't do that,' Mam says. 'It fair gives me t'creeps. It's enough to scrape th'hide off a donkey!'

'Wisht!' says Grandma. 'Nowt like a good scrat... It's little enough pleasure left to an owd woman!'

And I laugh, I laugh down into my dreams.

It's still dark when Dad goes to work. He looks in at my door: I can see him by the light shining through my open curtains. I say, 'Goodnight Dad.' He replies, *'Goodnight, sleep tight, mind the bugs don't bite!'* But this time he says nothing. He just looks and smiles. Now I really wake up. He stands there in his uniform – navy blue. He's a postman these days. Navy blue with black, plastic buttons. But NO! I shout 'MAM, MAM... IT'S NOT MY DAD!'

'You're dreaming,' she says. 'Go back to sleep... Your dad's in bed with me...'

But I'm not dreaming, I'm sitting up scared. It's not my dad, not his uniform, not even his old Air Force uniform. This one has buttons going up to his neck, and they're brass!

'MAM...'

Smiling at me still, he turns slowly and begins to go down the stairs. I can see his head going lower and lower with each step until he's out of sight, and the stairs don't creak at all...

It was my grandad, I think, the one from Liverpool...

Once I dreamed that my dad met me on the corner of New Crescent dressed up in his best suit.

'Quick!' he said. 'Run home. Somebody's died...'

Who can it be?' Only Mam or Grandma, one or the other. But it MUSTN'T be Mam...it MUSTN'T be Grandma. I run into the house. The fire burns in the sunlight. There's a coffin lying by the french window, and inside it there's my dad in his uniform, my dad!

'NO,' I shout. 'My dad's outside in his best suit! I've just seen him!' And out I run to find him. But he's not there. Just an empty street.

That's why I bought Grandma a full jar of Mint Imperials on her birthday. Three score and ten, she might die. She liked Mint Imperials, and the jar was full – thousands! She could hardly die while there was a Mint Imperial left in the jar, could she? I went up to her bedroom with it.

'What is it, love?' she asked, groping for her glasses. I screwed the top off and poured the mints out onto her quilt – oh, at least a thousand, a mint mountain! 'HAPPY BIRTHDAY, GRANDMA!' She looked scared. 'What are they?' she said.

'Your favourite, Grandma...MINT IMPERIALS!'

She laughed so hard she could have died!

∾

...always wanting something different...When Mam's off on her insurance round and Dad's out at work or at the chapel, I start my creep around the house, round every room, every cupboard...I read the newspaper clipping about my dad, when he came home from Africa. It tells me where he was with his ambulance, places with names I can't remember without looking – Benghazi, Mersa Matruh, Gambut – this is where those things happened that he won't ever talk about. I empty Mam's trinket trays and look very closely at every tiny little thing, rings, hairpins, a torment to look at. They make something happen in my head...a little scream in the distance.

~

'Mam! I need some treasure, I need sommat to hide!'

She digs around among her jewels, pulls out a necklace, a bracelet, some rings... 'Is this enough?'

'Yea!' I shout, and off I run to the old ditch with them. I crawl flat on my belly under the biggest hawthorn on the bank, and there I scratch out a hole that nobody could find, and there I ram down my treasure and cover it up.

One day, long after I've forgotten all about it, I'll go back under that hawthorn with a spade and I'll dig a hole, and there it'll be. Treasure!

~

One day, just after teatime, my dad thrust a hand into his uniform pocket and fished out a few coins. He stood them on edge, facing me, and one by one flicked them with his index finger. They rolled across to my hands. 'Pocket money!' he said.

Pocket money... That was something I'd never heard of, but now found the idea magical, enchanting. Almost at once I set out for the sweetshop on Rufford Road, just across from our Crescent. Cousin Eric was coming in the inward direction, so we crossed paths. He shook his head at my explanation of how to use pocket money.

'Better go to Woolworths,' he said. 'Get mis-shapes. They're better than anything in t'sweet shop, and they're cheap because they came out o' th'oven crooked!' Oh suddenly what a lovely world to live in! How could I not have known? So on Saturday morning I set off to town, walking so as not to waste money on bus fares. An expedition into Woolworths was never without some thrill – *something new* – and that day it happened. Some manager, God bless him, had put a stack of children's books next to the chocolate mis-shapes, and on top of that pile, in a white paper cover with large lettering inside a red border was the title:

HISTORY IN PICTURES

Volume 1

THE STONE AGE

Stone Age... What's Stone Age? Soon I know, soon I'm an expert, even before I get home on the bus. One shilling and sixpence... even cheaper than chocolate mis-shapes!

∾

History is the secret. I long to know what it means. I think it's written in shadows under the sycamores, or in the rust on the iron railings under the caretaker's black paint. They tell the truth. In the classroom, when shadows cover the windows and it starts to rain, then old books lying on windowsills tell the truth as well. I grab the book about Richard Lion Heart. He was in prison, and his minstrel, Blondel, searched for him all over Europe, going from castle to castle, singing a song that he and Richard had composed together... singing a song that he and Richard had composed together... *singing a song*... That's the truth, and if I say it again, I'll cry.

Sometimes I know I'm telling lies... I cheat. At playtime, when the lads are playing football, I sneak away through a gap in the fence. I'm thin, like a yard-and-a-half of pump water Grandma says, and I can squeeze through any gap, any missing railing's good for me! In the vicar's orchard behind the church I find the place where Stone Age men made their flint arrowheads. It's in a hollow behind a holly bush. That's a lie. Trouble is, there's no flint in Crossens. It's a village between the sea and the mere, built on a sand-bank. I use roof slate, purple's best, and rub it hard on bricks After a few days, I have an arrowhead, sharp, polished... I carry it around in my pocket for about a week, then bury it somewhere and pretend to forget. Later on, I find it again, and put it in my cupboard with the others.

I have to be careful. If they see me, they'll come up, sniggering.

'What's your middle name, Roy?' That's Strodger.

'I haven't got one.'

'O yes you have, doesn't he, lads?'

'O yea!' they say. 'Yea.' Nodding, nodding. Daren't ever contradict Strodger, even though they're all cousins.

'Your middle name's History. You're Mister History.' Posh voice for this. 'Didn't you know? We don't like history, do we, lads?... You're not like a real boy at all, Roy. Don't you know?' He butts with his head, growls like a dog. 'If I was you, I couldn't live with meself, I couldn't... Sorry to say it, but it's true...'

Yes, I know the truth, I know, I know... It's all because of the shoes somebody gave my mam, hand-me-downs, on her insurance round. 'Clean and decent!' she says, and Grandma says, 'O aye! Owt'll do for schoo!' No, no! Trouble is, they're dancing shoes.

'Them's girls' shoes,' Strodger says.

'They're boys' shoes, only shiny for dancing. Anyway, they make me wear 'em...'

'They wouldn't make me wear 'em!' he says. 'I'd daub 'em wi' paint, I'd kick 'em to bits quick!'

I don't care. I only care about the past. I don't daub 'em wi' paint, I don't kick 'em to bits... And I carry on living with myself, too, most of the time...

∾

Back kitchen... A BOOM like thunder.

'What's that, Grandma?' She stops still to listen.

'Thunder!' she snaps, and starts up again with her dolly stick. She doesn't believe in washing machines, not even if we had one. A dolly tub's the only way to get a good wash!

Again...another BOOM...Then three together, BOOM BOOM BOOM...And I know it isn't thunder. It's Banks Brass Band starting up with the big bass drum, I know what that means – the girls will practise their Morris dance on Rufford Road, and with luck their skirts will fly up above their knees, and...perhaps for once might fly higher...Eric says no, never. Them skirts will alus stay down, he says. It's because they sew lead weights around the hems. Lead weights! What a dreadful pity!

Still, rush out, watch them come prancing down the road like ponies. Purple skirts, little yellow waistcoats. Big girl in front, tossing a stick in the air. Band at the back, and behind them, the drum. Eric likes that big girl, but not me. I like some of the little ones, especially their knees if only I could see them long enough!

They pass in the rain, and the streamers from the pom-pom sticks, purple and yellow, fly away over their heads, and I run behind to get them for my collection. 'What for?' says Eric. 'They're only tissue paper!'

∾

...Yes...It's like the cigarette on Rufford Road, lying there in the rain, lit, lit and nobody in the street, a whole cigarette and smoke rising in a thin line...

I pick it up and run pell-mell to the toilets beside the library, and stand in the doorway to look at it. So beautiful because of the thin gold lines and the thin red lettering...GOLD LEAF...and I put it carefully to my mouth, and blow...

NOTHING! So what use is a cigarette? I ask Eric, but he just laughs, just laughs...

∽

The best place...*actually*...is sitting on the pavement under Willie Walter's sweetshop window. Like that, you can swizzle round when the girls come and watch them in the mirrors. The window is a big mirror, and every jar of sweets is a little mirror. If anybody sees you, they don't know what you're watching, the skirts, the knees. It's just a sweetshop window.

One Sunday morning Aunty Mary says, 'They say Willie Walter's started acting daft wi' lads...' And Eric says, 'If he acts daft wi' me, I'll smash him o'er his counter.'

'O dear!' Mam says. 'Well, we don't want to talk about that on the Sabbath, do we?'

So, so acting daft is worth a smash from Eric's famous fist...

But not another word was said.

∽

And one day I was sitting there waiting when Willie Walter stuck his head out and said, 'D'you like jelly babies?' I nodded yes. 'Well, there's a quarter here that somebody must have forgotten... You'd might as well take them.'

'Thanks!' I shouted, but I was still waiting for the girls.

'Well, come and get them, then!'

And then the door clicked shut behind me, and locked, and his arm went round my neck. I was choking.

'I've got you now, lad. I'm not joking you know.'

The trouble is, I was wearing those short pants made of grey shoddy, and the button holes get so worn that they just fly open for nothing. And then my weewee just falls out and lies there like a bit of string, and that's what happened next, while he was jerking his hand up and down in front of me. I thought of the dog I'd seen run over on Rufford Road, with its leg jerking like that, having a fit.

...so boring...What to do? Think? My secret thought.

...saw a man hit a boulder with a pickaxe...and there it was: perfect snake coiled inside the stone. Saw it just for a mo, just for a tick, perfect coiled snake green and brown, mouth wide open, even its eyes! And then it blew to dust...wondrousfossil...*fossil*...*fossil*...favouriteword... words...*wondrous*...

Willie Walter's gnarled hand...like bark...

'Get out, boy! Can't you see I'm closed!

I see him crumple over on his doorstep, start crying, wailing 'Jesus, O Jesus, help me, please...why don't you help me...'

And then I know – he's not just playing daft...He's mad! And all that, *all that*...because my fly buttons were loose!

After Willie Walter started acting daft, I shifted my custom to the new sweetshop in Preston New Road, until that, too, became another nightmare. The owner was an ex-Spitfire pilot who had been shot down. His face was made of steel or aluminium. He spoke to me only once: 'I can't laugh and I can't cry,' he said, and pulling down his shirt to expose his throat, he added, 'That's where my voice comes from.' It was a perforated disk like a telephone receiver.

I dreamed he was coming down New Crescent on a motorbike. 'Why don't you talk to me?' he shouted, but not with a human voice. It was a voice from a machine. I couldn't think of what to say. Nothing! I could only run. But this becomes Eric's story: 'There's a fella on Martin Mere who rides a BSA Bantam, chasing lads. "Hey you, lad, come 'ere!" he says. "I've got sommat to show yer." Then you have to run – just keep running, keep jumping over ditches. Don't let him catch up wi' you. He wears a long brown mac, and there's nowt underneath. I'll gie 'im a surprise one day if he chases me!'

And he did, he did. And when he got off his Bantam to chase Eric up Long Dyke, Eric gave a flying leap to the other side.

'O aye!' the man said. 'Two can play that game…'

He took his stance to make the leap. But he couldn't manage it. He had no choice but to keep running and cross over at a little concrete bridge, then run all the way back. Eric waited until he was a few feet away, then took another leap back again. 'Go on!' he taunted. But the man was winded. He could neither run nor jump. Eric picked up the BSA Bantam, lifting it over his head.

'Hey, you put that down!' the man wheezed. 'That's private property!'

'O aye?' Eric said, and flung it into the dyke, and with that story, my nightmare ended!

But Willie Walter went on and on, and we all heard the gossip. *We* heard it on the bus, sitting behind two of those old crones. He hired two big lads to help out in the shop. Well, you can imagine what that led to! O the police, the getting caught *In Fragrant Delito* whatever that means...

'O, with your pants down, I should think!'

'Well, in t'paper it led to that judge at Preston Crown Court shouting YOU ARE A MONSTER! at him.'

'Aye, that were when he asked for sixty or seventy *counts* to be taken into consideration!'

'My goodness me!'

(*Counts*?...Am I one of those?)

Silence for five minutes. The bus rattled on.

'But he did try, didn't he?'

'He did, he did!'

'... Churches, chapels ...'

'That's right! Churches, chapels...the synagogue...'

'Well, yes, naturally!'

Silence...yes...silence...

'And even a lady friend one time!'

'O yes, that's right, that's right!'

'On a tandem in matching outfits!'

Not silence this time, just giggling, giggling, and the bus rambling on. Me and Eric listening to every word we could catch. I'd seen them once, on the sea bank. I grabbed Patch to keep him from running at them, and held him tight while I watched. She lay on her back, and he kneeled over her, holding chocolates up and dropping them one at a time into her mouth. When they were all gone, they both jumped up, brushing down their outfits, got on the tandem, and off they went.

So that's what love's all about! I'd wondered.

('Monster,' that judge said! How did *he* know? What does a judge know about button-holes? What does *he* know about shoddy pants?)

Then off we go again:

'It's her I pity . . . Where'll she go now at her age?'

'I saw her sittin' on't door-step crying her eyes out.'

'Who'd be a mother, I ask you? D'you remember them cardigans she used to knit him, one sleeve to't th'elbow, and t'other near down to t'floor!

'O aye! And he used to dance around his shop in 'em, round and round . . .'

'O aye! He did! He did! . . . And He was grand at Christmas! Grand! I wonder where we'll get another Widow Twankey now . . .'

(That's where we got off.)

∾

One day, I come home from school to find Uncle Hugh, Aunty Mary and Eric sitting round the kitchen table grinning like Cheshire cats, the lot of them. Mam plonked the tea down on her best white cloth, and Aunty Mary pulled the latest *Visiter* out of her bag. In any other town in England, they'd call it *The Visitor*, but not in Southport. From day one it's been known as *The Visiter*.

'Our Roy's got history fever,' she said, and spreading out the newspaper pages, she began to read . . .

'*Crossens, a village with History, on the ancient coastal route between Liverpool and Preston . . .*'

'Not that Mam,' Eric said. 'Get to t'good bits!'

'Shurrup and listen! *In the churchyard is a boulder of no*

mean size, dropped there by the last glacier as it made its way slowly across Lancashire...'

'How did it get through t'gate?' Dad joked.

'Gate weren't there!' said Uncle Hugh. 'Nowt there, I shouldn't wonder!'

'The dugout, Mam, the dugout!' Eric hissed.

'I KNOW!' said Aunty Mary. 'I'm leading up to it. Now just listen! *A cannonball, recently dug up in Brade Street, provides mute witness to an unrecorded skirmish of the Civil War...'*

'Aye, but what abaht King Arthur?' Uncle Hugh put in.

'That's fairy tales, that is! This is History...'

'Some do say as he threw Excalibur into t'mere... Our Roy could dig it up!' He chuckled, thinking of the ten thousand fields of Martin's Mere between Crossens and Ormskirk.

'Why did he chuck it away?' Dad said. 'Was it bust?'

'It were enchanted,' Eric said. 'He had to chuck it in t'water...'

'SHURRUP YOU LOT! Shurrup and listen.' She adjusted her specs, and with a sly grin at me she went on: *'There is ample proof that Stone Age man once navigated the waters of Martin's Mere...'*

My heart stopped. How was it possible? My astonishment must have been visible, because Eric started laughing behind his hands and kicking me under the table.

'*...as we can see from the prehistoric dugout canoe in the museum at the Botanic Gardens...* There! What d'you say to that, our Roy?'

I could say nothing. I was ashamed, ashamed and delighted in the same instant. I didn't know where to look.

Eric was sympathetic at last. 'It's not your fault!' he said.

'Nobody notices it. It's behind a door, and it looks like an old tree trunk!'

How often had I been in that museum, poring over the shrunken head, the toy soldiers and the stuffed birds . . . and now I discover that all the time they have had a prehistoric dugout canoe from Martin's Mere – the very place where we were sitting, living, sleeping, and which we could see by just walking round our Crescent to the dyke and opening our eyes! Well, never mind! They had a dugout canoe. It really existed. So I wasn't just a soft lad who had dreams and who lived in make-believe. I was an archaeologist! Or at least, I would be soon.

∾

One of those Sundays, I could see something special had happened. Eric came round, and we had cream cakes on the white cloth.

'Where's Aunty Kitty?' I shouted. Mam said nowt for a while, then she bethought herself to speak . . . 'O, didn't you know? . . . She's off to Glasgow with Bill to get married.'

Know? I did NOT know! I'd never thought of such a thing. Eric kicked me under the table. He lay with his chin on the cloth and his hands cupped around his mouth. 'They've eloped!' he hissed.

'They've what?'

'ELOPED.' Aah . . . So *that's* what it means . . .

And we squirmed in an ecstasy of astonished delight!

They sent us a letter from Cathcart, near Glasgow. Bill said, *To Mrs Howard, every good wish*. To me, a postcard with a picture of the tartan of Bill's clan, Clan Fraser. To

Grandma, a letter to tell her that, in Glasgow, you can't buy a lettuce for love nor money!

Grandma set up a wail. 'What'll we do? She can't live all her life without a lettuce!' So we make a plan. Every Sunday, Uncle Hugh brings one of his lettuces, and we wrap it up in a copy of *The Southport Visiter*, tie it with string, and put a luggage label on with the address. Next day, Dad takes it to the GPO and sends it off. When it arrives, their postman takes a peek, and when he delivers it he says, 'Another lettuce, Mrs Fraser. You're happy now, I daresay!'

I start spending my Saturday mornings in the little Victorian museum in the Botanic Gardens, now I know about the canoe. I creep around in silence from room to room. I'm usually the only one there, except for the man in uniform and the cleaning woman. I don't want them to follow me. DO NOT TOUCH, the signs say. Why not? I want to touch things, stroke things, let their stories come inside me. The canoe was found in Martin Mere by a vicar. There's a photo of him watching a farmer bring it to the museum on his cart. When I've memorised the canoe again, I slip down the stairs to the landing with the suit of armour. This is difficult, because they keep watching me. I don't know the armour as well as I know the canoe. CAP A PIE 1485. This sign is a mystery, but I'm beginning to memorise the armour and the long sword. I want to copy it, make it out of tin cans...cut them up with Mam's shears, sew them together with baling wire...

Outside on the steps, the headache comes, striking suddenly, a blow from a black hammer, hurls me into a wide room of darkness where dark is all pain. How? What have I done? I've been staring too long into armour, looking too urgently into its secrets. Now I'm punished by my frantic need to understand, to know everything...Why don't I leave things alone?

I stumble down the steps, bent double, arms covering my head. Can't stand the sunlight. Worse crossing over the little bridge, crossing the serpentine, light gleaming off the water. Down on my knees I crawl over, then up the bank of hard earth towards the red wall in shadow where I hide my eyes and lie, suffering the pain. Tree roots under me. Can't tell how long I lie or whether I sleep. Suddenly there is a voice cutting into my darkness.

It's Eric. 'What're you doing there? We've been looking everywhere for you.'

I try to say the one word – *headache*...

'Come on!' he says. 'I'll take you home on the cross-bar.' And he rides his bike *whistling...whistling*...It's the Devil who torments me with that whistling, and I can't do anything to stop it.

'Where was he?' Dad says.

'Lying against the wall in the Botanic.'

'*Headache*,' I say, a frantic whisper. '*Headache...bed... armour...sorry...*'

'It's all right,' Mam says. 'Here's an aspirin. Who are you apologising to?'

'God, I think, Mam...Goodnight...'

An illness was going round. We were all getting it, one

time or another. Strodger got it, and when he came back, he was full of himself. He'd spent all day thinking up poems. He makes us all gather round to listen. You have to. This is one:

> *long and thin, goes right in*
> *made to please the ladies*
> *short and thick, does the trick*
> *and produces babies*

'O Strodger, you only think about one thing,' Billy Dee says.

'Well,' says Strodger. 'Wharelse is there? Wharelse, I ask you?'

Then it's his joke...His jokes are even worse than his poems. Here's the one about the lass stuck in the farmer's field.

There are four gates to the field with a farmer's lad at every gate. She goes to the first gate and asks can I get out. Not till you gie me a bit he says. She goes to the second gate and asks can she get out. Not till you gie me a bit he says. She goes to the third gate and asks can she get out. Not till you gie me a bit he says. She goes to the fourth gate and gie's him a bit and he lets her out!

'D'you ger it?' he hisses. Nobody does.

'It's not worth talkin' to you lot' he says. 'You don't get nowt...Watch!'

He draws the field, the gates, the path taken by the girl from gate to gate...'NAH d'yer ger it?...It's all to do wi' sixty-nine!' Then we're supposed to laugh. If we don't, he gets mad and starts scrapping. He gets into a fit, he can't stop, he can't let loose. He's like a dog once he gets going.

'Ask her!' he says. 'Go on, ask her if you don't believe me! Just go up and say, "Was it nice on Saturday?" I dare you!' They took her to Nuck's Wood, that's what he says...her hands tied behind her back...

Barbara, one of the nicest girls in school. I don't believe him, but I watch her. I dwell on her. When she walks down by the old ditch, I follow her through the nettles. There's a water rat, its snout creases the gloom-filled water... When it turns into a stage-coach, I know I'm dreaming.

∾

Rain pricks my face, starts me laughing deep down, deeper than my throat, like the jokes in dreams that are too funny to remember, but later, when you think of them, those thoughts are like stabs of sadness.

I'm carrying the school bell. 'Pop it in the Headmaster's study, Roy,' Mr Dobbins said. But he didn't say which way to go! I take the long way, so I can hide under the syca-mores and wait there until Sarah Threlfall comes. She's late. The morning hymn has started:

> Holy Holy Holy
> Lord God Almighty
> Cherubim and Seraphim
> And all the Saints adore Him...

I watch Sarah Threlfall. I adore *her!* Sometimes she's late, she never hurries. I'll wait, in the rain, under the leaves. I'll get wet through. I don't say *beautiful* – but I think it a lot. Everything about Sarah Threlfall is beautiful, everything! I don't know why. I pray for rain, so she'll wear her gaberdine. Then she'll have her fingers slipped into the pockets, but not her thumb, that's always outside. The hood just doesn't quite cover her hair. She never wears welly boots, just black slip-ons with hard, thin soles. When she swivels in at the gate, they scrape the pavement, and her mac parts at the bottom – that button's never fastened – and her heel comes up out of the shoe for a moment, and then her knee just under her skirt just visible as she gives the gate a shove. The steel latch sings. She takes ten paces to the girls' porch, looking down at the puddles. She doesn't look at me, but she knows I'm here. Then I watch the rain cover her footprints.

'Goodness, Roy, get a move on!' Mr Dobbins says – but he's smiling. *He knows!* 'Just slip through the girls' porch...'

Girls' porch, three rows of gaberdines, and the last still wet. I breathe deep – dare I touch it? Slide my fingers into the pocket?

I'd like to ring the bell! This is the Bell of Praise, the bell to praise Sarah Threlfall! Listen... I'll make it ring somewhere.

Then I'll be famous!

5

'What's that?... Goodness me, is it the Stone Age?'

Miss Drewitt had seen me going through the fence, and now she'd followed me. That *was* a surprise!

'Have you got a spark yet?'

I shook my head and stood up. 'Can't get sparks without flint, Miss. There's no flint in Crossens.' I handed her the tool in my hand, copied from the picture in my book, the picture in my head.

'It's a harpoon, Miss...five barbs...it's for fishing.'

'Oh, I'll remember that! Harpoon...Thank you! Now let's get back into the playground, shall we? This is the vicar's orchard, you know!'

'Yes Miss.' I'm afraid she'll tell! But when we line up to go into school, she says nowt about the orchard, but I hear her say to Old Slater, 'That child is positively morbid!' And Old Slater replies, 'Try to get him involved in some healthy activity, Miss Drewitt.' I don't know *morbid*, but I do know *healthy activity* – he means football, of course.

Football! Don't they know I'm no good at football? It's partly my boots to blame. Mam bought me a pair five sizes too big, so they'd last till I leave school in five years. Aunty Mary calls them 'Our Roy's football *boats*' and Mam says, 'Well, I'm not buying football boots every five minutes...He'll have to make do!' That means stuffing newspaper in the toes.

'Aye!' Dad says. 'That's all well and good. But, you see, he has to kick a ball, and you can't kick a ball with newspaper in the toes, you don't know where it'll go.'

He was right about that, Dad. The one time I did get to have a kick, I was right near the net and the goalie was flat on his face in the mud. Nobody near – a goal, a goal for sure! I closed my eyes and belted that ball as hard as I could. Everything went quiet. I looked round. No ball in sight. Not in the net, not behind the net...and when

I turned round, I saw both teams, all of them, rolling on the ground laughing their heads off, and even Mr Halsall, who couldn't blow the whistle for laughing, was staggering from side to side, like to fall over . . . And there, finally, I saw the ball. It must have gone up in the air, come back over my head, and fallen down right at my heels. Yes, it was very funny, I suppose. And it was very sad.

Shame haunts me, poisons everything. Eric tells his mam that he's sick of seeing me dragging myself around the playground by myself looking miserable. Mam says it's not natural, and Aunty Kitty asks me if I'm unhappy at school.

After that, I stay in the front playground so Eric won't see me. I only want to be alone.

Into the midst of this long loneliness, came something new . . . I heard my name. I was in the front playground, in the corner under the sycamores, in the shadows. It was something from the wind, the breeze, something from a bird, a swallow's wing. It had never happened before.

That gave me sommat to think about! It happened again after the bell, when we were lining up to go into school. That time, I glanced around – surely someone else had heard it, too – but no! Behind me, Little Aughtie stared blankly into space. It was clear that he'd not heard a thing – that little word . . . ROY . . . but so soft. It's a message . . . *It must be meant for me!*

A mystery like this in Crossens . . . How could anybody believe it? It isn't a place in the Bible, where people are always hearing messages. It's just an old fishing village on the Ribble, not like Galilee, not like anywhere with a burning bush...Even on Bonfire Night there's no message in the fire. At home, I decided I was imagining things. I tried to make it happen. All weekend I went to different places – the recreation ground, the marshes, Martin's Mere – I walked all over the place trying to hear my name...but I never heard a thing! It happened only at school – and only to me! I began to feel worried. I cornered Brian Rimmer in the porch and asked him whether he'd heard a voice whispering names. He gave me a strange look and said no. I no longer enjoyed this mystery. But what could I do? Nothing helped. Prayers were no use. I felt miserable.

My condition must have been visible, and it wasn't only Eric who saw it. On my way home from school, my cousin Glenys came up alongside me and asked if everything was all right. O yes! I lied, *everything's all right.* Then I thought again. Why not confide in Glenys? She was the eldest cousin, a year older than Eric. She was a saved soul who had seen the light. She carried her Bible with her everywhere she went. I followed her home, and she led me into the back garden. I sat down on an upturned bucket in the middle of Uncle John's potatoes. Glenys dragged up an old garden chair and sat facing me, holding my hands. O yes! She knew something was wrong. After all, that was her vocation. Though only thirteen, she was the self-appointed Saint of Crossens.

'First, let's ask for help,' she said, and closed her eyes.

'O Lord, who speakest out of fire, out of whirlwind, speak now to us, and to my little cousin, Roy...*Lead us, Heavenly Father lead us, o'er the world's tempestuous sea...Guard us, guide us, keep us, feed us, For we have no help but Thee . . . Lone and dreary, faint and weary, through the desert Thou dids't go* . . . Now Roy, what's all this about?'

Glenys has a way with her, but I'm used to this of course. I know the prayers, the hymns. Mam and Dad both preach, now, in various chapels, Grandma sings hymns every night of her life, and Grandad died with a hymn on his lips, didn't he? I'm used to saints. I live with them. It's funny, but I sometimes think I could be a saint myself. It comes over me in chapel, or even with the morning hymn in school, that feeling that I could just cut myself loose and drift up like an angel into the light and disappear through a high window. But I can't tell what will happen next.

Now, I take a deep breath, and shamelessly I blurt out: 'I've heard a voice.'

'A voice? What sort of voice?'

'A soft whisper, like the wind, and it says my name . . .'

'Are you sure you're not imagining it, Roy?'

'I'm not imagining it. I've tried everything to imagine it, and it doesn't work. I've tried everything to get rid of it, and that doesn't work either.'

She swayed over me for a few moments, looking and thinking.

'Is it a still, small voice, Roy? Are you being called?'

I nodded. O yes! That had to be true. I was being called.

'Have you answered?'

No, I hadn't answered. It hadn't occurred to me to answer. Glenys shook her head slowly. 'Now you must answer, Roy . . . You must say, *Speak Lord, Thy servant heareth* . . .'

'Glenys, do you think it might be . . . History?'

She looked hard and shook her head. 'History doesn't call, Roy. History's the past, that's all. It's God who calls ... well, either God or the Devil ... but I doubt whether it could be the Devil in our family, could it?'

I shook my head. I couldn't think of any devil it could be.

'And will you answer next time, Roy?'

I nodded. Yes, I knew what to say.

'I'll pray for you!' she said.

I heard it twice, once in the cloakroom and once in the classroom. The first time, I shouted out, 'SPEAK LORD ...' But I heard nothing but the boys fighting over the coat hooks. In the classroom, it was silent. Miss Oswick was hunched over her desk, and we were supposed to be writing. I heard it clear! And despite everything, I knew I had to answer, and not just with a whisper ... I had to shout. I didn't manage that, but I did speak, quite clearly: 'Speak Lord ... Thy servant heareth!'

'Who spoke? Which of you spoke?

I raised my hand.

'And what did you say?'

'Speak Lord, Thy servant heareth ...'

'And who were you speaking to, Roy?'

'Jesus, Miss.'

She looked down at her desk, and sat like that for a long time. At last she said, 'Well, He isn't here just now. Carry on with your work.'

On Monday, I went to school more prepared, with the little red New Testament Mam had given me for my ninth birthday in my pocket. And then what happened, what blessed thing filled the school, the playground, my soul? – NOTHING! All day waiting for it, and nothing! Silence! It had come to an end! I was glad! I was happy, happy, HAPPY!

But had I passed the test?

A month went by, and I forgot about the whispers. I was back with my own affairs – I was left alone when I slipped through the fence into the vicar's orchard, and my skill with purple slate grew daily. I never used modern tools – no steel! Just stones and slates. After school, I started trying to make bits of armour, using the tin cans, mostly dog-food tins, that I cut up with Mam's dress-making shears.

A month, I should have guessed! A month of scarlet fever. That explained the blessed silence. I found out one morning after playtime. I'd stayed too long in the orchard and missed the bell. Before going inside, I went into the boys' urinal, and I was spraying pee up high against the black tarred wall. I heard someone come in behind me. 'Making trees, are you?' he said. Then, before I could say a word in reply, he was up behind me, clinging, grabbing at my balls, spitting and slavering over my neck. Urine ran down my legs, soaking into my socks. I couldn't shake him off. It was like the worst nightmares – the electric water, the biting dog whose teeth stick in the skin, the leeches that drag things out of you when you try to pull them off. *It was no game!*

All the time as he clung on me, he whispered and hissed in a frantic, fast tirade. '*Speak Lord* ... It was me, not Jesus, me all the time. Listen, listen ... It's time to tell you my plan ... my plan what I'm going to do wi' you. All the time I was ill, I've thought o' nowt else. I hate you, you make me sick, every time I look at you ... can't get you off my mind ... I'm going to tell you when nobody's looking ... my plans.'

And it was as though nothing had happened – he was gone, and I was left crushed and trembling against that stinking wall.

Who was he? I didn't know him, other than as a boy in my class. Teachers called him Phillip, we used the nickname Crisps. He was small and well-dressed, polite, good in school. He was also another of Strodger's clan of cousins. For me, he was a little corner of Hell. How clever he was! He knew by some instinct that I would never utter a word of his doings to anyone, and that I would do nothing to defend myself against his acts and insults. Day after day it went on…his plans. He watched me all the time, waiting until he could get close enough to start whispering without anyone else hearing or noticing. He'd found books hidden under his parents' bed in an old suitcase – books by Lord Russell of Liverpool which describe tortures, rapes and murders committed in prison camps by Hitler's gangs and Japanese soldiers.

'I'm going to do wi' you what Hitler did to Jews,' he said, again and again. He talked about piano wire and butchers' meat-hooks. One day in class, he caught my eye and slid a hook out of his pants' pocket onto the seat where I could see it. He said he'd stolen it when the butcher wasn't looking, and he'd hidden some more in secret places ready for the time, *the time*…He knew some furniture movers who would get him an old piano for the wire. He knew how to do such things – he'd seen the photographs. 'It's real,' he'd say. 'It's history…it's what Hitler did to Jews.'

No way to make him stop…His words keep coming back, they drown every other word, thinking themselves over in my mind until I cry. I must have other thoughts

– now when storm clouds loom at the high windows and Miss Johnson puts her finger on the light switch, *Stop thought...stop thought...stop...think something else, think foxglove...soft on a finger...soft...soft...think fox...glove...*

So it went on and on until the last day of the school term, the last day before summer holidays. And that day brought something new. First, a stone hit my back. That was in the playground. I turned around. A girl stood a few feet away, leaning towards me, hissing. Behind her, a group of girls – just a few boys as well – were pulling faces and making gestures.

'Is that him?' one of them shouted.

'Yea, that's him, and he's bloody big an' all!'

Some more stones, luckily thrown by the girls. Then I see him at the back of the crowd. Amazing! He's crying, wailing, covering his head with his arms, tottering back and forth... 'O Roy, I'm sorry,' he wails – 'I know we're not supposed to tell tales, but I can't stand it any more.' Now he flails his arms around his head as though he's in agony. 'You've driven me mad...I'm losing my mind...'

Now Strodger comes up. 'You can't keep on bullying little lads forever, Roy!' he says. 'I didn't bully anybody,' I reply. 'That's not what Crisps says, is it?' He appeals to the crowd.

So there has to be a big fight after school. A big fight. This doesn't concern me much, since my cousin Eric can defend me against the lot of them. But Crisps has already thought of this – and suddenly he's stopped wailing and crying, and he's quite in control of himself, eager to get a general agreement for this big fight. He's had words with Eric – who, as everyone knows, is a strong believer in fair play, and who has agreed...*agreed*...to be the referee.

Poor Eric! There he was at four o'clock, outside the school gate looking almost dead with shame. Crisps was dashing around frantically reminding everybody that *he* was the victim, that he was having nightmares because I'd threatened to kill him and hang his remains on meat-hooks. Most of the school was waiting there – all ages, from toddlers to sneering twelve-year-olds. I saw this from the porch, and realised that I would have to pass through the centre of Hell. I perceived the scene in both the minutest detail and simultaneously as a vague cloud of meaningless motion. I didn't care what they thought. I wanted to go home, so I walked towards them.

The crowd parted, making a long funnel of spitting, jeering faces with Crisps right at the end waving his clenched fists up and down and stamping his feet like a mechanical doll. He was wearing a bright orange jersey that day. I tried to see beyond him to the horizon, the next Ice Age. At the end of the funnel, I had to stop. Then some big lad was holding me by the shoulders, saying, 'Why won't you fight?' I thought about the question, and answered, 'I'm not angry.'

'What if he hits you, will that make you angry?'

'I don't know.'

I hear a dull bang at the back of my head. Then another. I wasn't sure what had caused them, but some droplets of blood were falling at my feet. Crisps was dancing around in the road shouting, 'I've won! You must admit I've won!'

But no one was taking any notice now. Strodger had walked off by himself, and little groups of girls were moving away, clutching each other. I continued walking. Eric caught up with me. 'You lost!' he says. I say, 'I didn't fight...'

'Did you really bully him?'

I shake my head. 'Of course not...He was the one who did all those things to me. I was just trying to ignore him!'

It all ended that day. Why? I never found out. But Crisps never glanced in my direction again, and not one of those girls ever again made any accusation of such a thing against me.

A long lifetime later, my mother, bedridden and slowly dying, murmured one morning, 'You had a bully, didn't you...but we soon fixed that, didn't we?' Really? Well, if so, whatever action was taken, it certainly did not come *soon*. I rather suspect she was confusing me with my Uncle Dick. When he was bullied, Grandma bought him a pair of clogs, and said 'Gie him a good kicking, that'll fix it!' And it did.

6

A foxglove falls. We all know – we hear that tiny sound as the flower breaks from its stem, and drops on the window-sill...We all want it, *soft on a finger*, but who will get it?

This moment...*now*...is almost three o'clock on Friday. Miss Oswick was chuntering to herself a few minutes ago. Now she's almost asleep in her desk. We wait for the bell. I'm watching Sarah Threlfall's foot, which has strayed out of her desk and now lies in the aisle, showing her knee and her calf and, of course, her ankle sock and the shiny black shoe. I'm also trying to imagine the mysterious greens of Sherwood Forest, and hear the flashing arrows across the glade. How can I draw a flying arrow? Crayons are useless...

'Please Miss,' Wendy pipes up. That girl has no respect for silence! 'Can I have the foxgloves that have fallen off?'

Miss Oswick murmurs 'Yes,' and Wendy slides from her desk and drops to her knees. How do girls do these things? We all want it, but only a girl would just *ask*!

'Hey!' Strodger hisses. 'Gie's one for my little finger, and not a withered-up one, neither!' He threatens with his fist. But Wendy just glances towards Miss Oswick, then sticks her tongue out at him, sticks it out and wiggles it around. We know what *that* means – no foxglove for Strodger!

The door was slightly open. That was strange. But, O! the reason passed among us by glimpse and glance – Old Slater was just outside spying on Miss Oswick! Some of the girls coughed and banged their desks to wake her up.

'Friday afternoon, Miss Oswick!' he said. 'We don't want them to fall asleep, do we?'

'No, Headmaster...'

'No indeed!' And he rapped on one of the front desks with his swagger stick. As the day was hot and sunny, he was wearing his jungle whites. 'Now, boys and girls, I'm going to tell you something very important...' And aside to Miss Oswick, he said, 'This is the sort of thing to do on a Friday, Miss Oswick...'

He drew a triangle on the blackboard, narrow at the top and wide at the bottom. That, he said, was adequate for a sketch map of the British Isles. We then, in answer to his questions, established the cardinal points, noting especially our own position in the WEST. 'Now, children, what would you think if I were to tell you that in the EAST of our beloved land, the erosion of soil is causing the coastline to shrink at a rate of about four inches per year! Now that may not sound like very much. But think, in a thousand years, ten thousand years, a million years...those four inches per year would amount to several miles! Now, children, do you really believe that our Lord God in His wisdom would allow this land, this beloved land, to diminish?' And he threw back head and laughed. 'No, no, no...boys and girls.' And he tapped the WEST with the end of his stick. 'You see, for every INCH that He taketh away in the East, He giveth a FOOT in the WEST!...Now, what lessons could we draw from this, children?'

Big Billy Dee raised his hand at once. 'It means that God likes us more than them, sir!' he said. Our headmaster groaned and turned his back to us, and when he swung round to face us once again, he had turned into a lunatic, prancing from foot to foot and swiping at desks with his stick. It was to be a 'shake-up', he said. We all had to empty our desks and stand to attention. Then we were moved to new places, two by two, until we all had a different desk and a new neighbour.

'There we are, Miss Oswick!' he said. 'Don't let them fall asleep!'

He departed. We dared not speak, but we *looked!* She knew, of course. 'Stay where you are...'

'But Miss!'

'Silence! Stay where you are for now...Just carry on.'

Before, I'd always had a double desk to myself, and now I had to share. It was a curious thing. I'd been moved next to a boy called Derek Hesketh who was new to the school and also new to our Crescent. Like me, he seemed to be an only son, and the Heskeths' house was directly opposite ours. I saw them arrive from my bedroom window, where I was arranging and memorising my collection of tartan post-cards from Cathcart. The removal men had almost finished when a car arrived – a famous kind of car. People who liked to show off their knowledge of cars used to say it was the best British car on the road – a Humber Hawk, and black, the first car ever seen in New Crescent except for a few taxis. The boy and the man slid out from the front seat and helped the other person – mother or grandmother? – out from the back seat. She was bent double, completely covered with a large shawl. They all moved slowly into the house, both man and boy cradling the woman in their arms.

After that, I hardly ever saw the father and his car. I may have seen the woman once. It was a night of bright, full moon, and we walked back from the pictures, getting home very late. I never drew my curtains and so, by that moonlight and the street lamps, I saw someone clearly enough, though it seemed strange. She was kneeling on their new lawn with a little torch and a pair of scissors. Who could she be, but his mother?

Derek used to walk to school on the shop side of Rufford Road, and I on the graveyard side. Coming home after school, as by unspoken agreement, we swapped sides. I was satisfied by that, as I could run through the churchyard in the morning and stroke the granite boulder when no one was around, and after school I could smell the bunches of new bicycle tyres hanging up in the hardware shop doorway. I assumed he'd come from a private school because he always wore a blazer with a school badge on the pocket, though it was a scruffy blazer with patches on the elbows. So he was safe from bullies.

It became clear that Miss Oswick was not going to

make any evaluations of our drawings on this particular occasion. All we had to do was remain still and quiet. I was glad – my attempt to discover the moods of Sherwood Forest was failing. I glanced over at my neighbour, hoping he had not looked first. I was embarrassed. But at that glance, I turned dizzy, breathless: *There was someone else like me...*

His drawing was a lake village in the Stone Age. It was like the drawings in my book of the Neolithic villages in the Swiss lakes. I turned my piece of paper over, and wrote: *Lake village in the Stone Age.* I slid it towards him, and he looked at it for a moment. Then he drew the paper within the shield of his arm for a long moment before sliding it back. I read:

> No, not Stone Age.
> AFRICA
> Yours sincerely,
> Derek Hesketh
> PS. Africa is still in the Stone Age.

Then, as our eyes met, he glanced down to where he had a secret book pinned under the desk by his knees, and pulled it over his lap so that I could see the scene: yes, it was in Africa, and it was something like the Stone Age...

Outside, I lingered on Rufford Road, hoping he would not cross to the other side. At last he caught up with me, and we fell against each other, arms around each other's neck...stumbled into the churchyard wall, staggered into the gutter, loitered in circles...and he opened his fist – *foxgloves...*

'How did you...' I began.

'I followed her. She chucked 'em away once she was out of school. I knew she would.'

And all the way down Rufford Road, the soft beauty of those flowers mesmerised our eyes.

'Get a move on, you boys!' Cauliflower barked, as she pedalled past us on her old sit-up-and-beg. 'Don't loiter!'

'Yes Miss,' we replied in unison.

'D'you think they loiter in Africa?' I murmured.

'Of course they do. Well known. It's an African custom.'

'Good... Let's loiter some more then...'

∾

I soon learned that Derek was in love with Africa as much as I was with the Stone Age. And he had some advantages – Africa was still there. He was planning his first expedition already, though he would not leave until he was eighteen. That seemed very sensible, he said. Boys can do anything by the time they reach eighteen! In the meantime, he had nine years to plan, to collect ideas, and – most important – to learn the language.

'It's a pity you can't go to the Stone Age,' he said

'I know, I think about that all the time... But instead I just pretend I'm there...'

'What can you plan for instead of just pretending?'

'I can learn archaeology, I suppose... Go digging things up.'

'That's very good,' he said. 'Very very good... You've got practical ideas as well!'

Derek had many practical ideas. Among them, he had

various schemes for avoiding bullies – some just like mine – but his speciality was in making plans. Lying in the long grass beside our dyke, or at the Three Legs, a tidal marker out on Crossens marsh, we made *our* plans – the plans for our friendship. In school, we would keep it secret. We'd keep apart in classrooms and in the playground. After school, we'd loiter in the road until no other pupils were left, and then meet up in the village library.

The underlying notion to our rules was that there is weakness in numbers – two times weak equals *very* weak – whereas a single victim can always find a place to hide, such as in the vicar's orchard! We assumed, of course, that Miss Oswick would not enforce Old Slater's changes to our normal places, and indeed she did not.

The little village library was a good place to hide, especially on days of rain and thunder. One of those evenings, while searching as usual for some books for Grandma with 'R' on the spine, I made an astonishing discovery – Crossens was the repository of all the county archaeological collections, huge, magnificent books arranged along the highest shelves. I could reach them with the little ladder on wheels until the librarian saw me.

'Children must not touch, must NOT touch, must NOT climb the ladder...'

'Looking for a book for my grandma,' I explained.

'What? On archaeology?'

'No Miss... that was for my dad...'

'Well then, he must come and search himself!'

When I told Dad over our tea, he said, 'None of her business!' And after that he gave me a note and one of his tickets, and I was free to take whatever I fancied.

Derek just kept renewing the same books on Africa and Swahili. What did it matter when no one else had placed it on order. When the woman told him he should stop that, he explained that it takes a long time to learn a language, and he still had many pages of vocabulary to learn. 'Shall I bring a note, Miss?' he asked. She said, 'Yes, bring a note from your mother.' So he agreed, so long as he could keep the books for another month.

When Derek spoke of his *ambition* to speak Swahili, I realised at once that I, also, had an *ambition*...to speak Welsh.

'Granny and Grandad in Liverpool used to speak Welsh all the time,' I told him, 'and Grandma keeps looking at her mother's Welsh Bible every morning in bed, trying to remember it...' But it had never occurred to me before that moment that a book could perhaps exist on how to speak Welsh, and it could perhaps be in the library...And it was! TEACH YOURSELF WELSH it was called. Well, what a thrill! It was as though everything I could think of suddenly came into existence.

'Now we have to encourage each other!' Derek said. 'Let's learn ten words every week and test each other on Saturday.'

That was a good idea. I knew that I could memorise things quite easily. I'd already memorised the ages of the Stone Age, the parts of a suit of armour, and a lot of tartans, so ten words a week should have been easy. But when it came to Welsh, it wasn't so easy. According to my book, one word in English could become several words in Welsh because of something called *mutation*, which I could not understand at all. How could anybody believe that the word for 'father' was *four* words, all beginning with a different letter! But according to this book, that was true – the words were TAD, DAD, THAD, and NHAD. But when it came to MOTHER, there are only *two* words – MAM and FAM. By the time Saturday came, I had secretly decided that the book was telling lies!

When we met in the street, I confessed my fears and suspicions, indicating the strange lists in my book. Derek stared at them. 'But *mam* and *dad* are English, too!' he said. Yes, that was another problem – why the English words, then the different first letters? 'D'you think it might be lies?' I said. He shook his head. 'I think there must be something we don't understand,' he said. But some phrases had caught his eye – 'Hey! It tells you how to ask for a cup of tea! That's in my Swahili, too!' We found them, compared them, and started trying to pronounce the phrases over and over until we didn't need the books.

'Come on!' he said. 'Let's try it on my mum.' Seeing my surprise, he added, 'She's fun, my mum...' Well, *that* was something! No one ever said *mum*, because mum was almost the same as mummy, and you could be killed for saying that! He'd said it, and he knew I'd heard... That was a true sign of friendship.

I followed him around to the back door. It was very confusing. In the first place, I wasn't used to being invited into anyone's house. I went to Aunty Mary's and Aunty Phyllis's as a matter of course, but to nowhere else. And the idea of a grown-up being *fun* was even stranger. Grandma did things like sword-fight, but I kept that secret from everybody. It was hard to admit, but Grandma was as good as Errol Flynn. And when I complained that she cheated, she'd just laugh and turn back to the sink. But Grandma was unique – there could not be anyone else like *her* in our universe!

'Mum, this is Roy,' he said. She was at the sink. She wore a high pinnie like Grandma's, and her hair was braided and gathered in a bun on the back of her head, with a foot or so of loose hair falling over her shoulder. She turned and smiled, wiping her hands on the pinnie. 'Hello Roy,' she said, holding out her hand. More surprises...In the first place, I now realised that I'd never seen her before, or at least not face to face. Also, she was beautiful...beautiful like the most beautiful heroines in films. And she was shaking my hand, which was something that had never happened to me before. 'Derek has told me a lot about you. He says you like history?'

At this point, my friend gave me the nod. I didn't want to do it now, but I had to: *'Ga I cwpanaid o de, os gwelwch yn dda?'*

Those were the words, but only God could know how I pronounced them. She dropped her head to one side, and placed her hands on her hips. Derek began to laugh, and said: 'TAFADHALI NIPATIE KIKOMBE CHAI.' Now she tossed the apron aside and fell to her knees. 'What is this? What are you saying?' Derek had dropped to his knees also, in front of his mother, and they laughed so hard that their heads banged together: 'IT'S WELSH,' he shouted, 'WELSH AND SWAHILI...' A moment later, he was writhing all over the kitchen floor as she tickled him, while I stood helplessly at attention by the back door. I was, doubtless, bright red and absolutely lost. They stood up and got control of themselves. They, too, were blushing.

Her long braid had come loose, and hung down almost to her knees.

'Yes, Roy...Derek says you like History...Let's have tea!'

We talked about clothes. She was astounded that Derek preferred his threadbare blazer to the nice new one hanging in the wardrobe. We told her the facts of life in Crossens: old clothes are much better than new ones. Derek had already told her about my dancing shoes, and she didn't think it mattered in the least whether they were shiny or not. We put her straight on that, telling her just how much it mattered! And a cap! Well, the best thing would be to throw it in the old ditch. And socks, yes, we need them, but not pulled up, NEVER pulled up, and without garters. By the time I left, she was much wiser. I showed off, too, I showed off shamelessly, reciting the names of the geologic ages and the Stone Age cultures associated with them: *Creswellian, Magdalenian, Solutrean, Gravettian, Aurignacian, Châtelperronian, Mousterean* ...

'GOSH!' she said.

Over the following weeks, Derek told me a lot about his mum. She wasn't like us: she came from a wealthy family, and she had a middle name that was French. She'd attended a finishing school in Switzerland. She hated it, and ran away when she was eighteen and was disinherited. During the war, she fell in love with her dad's driver and married him. When Derek was born, she went home with the baby in her arms, and they wouldn't let her inside. Derek said he didn't care. *She* didn't care either. They liked being poor – it was more fun. Poor folk have to think about the things they need, they don't just buy everything! The only thing she disliked about living on a council estate was being looked at. That's why she covered her head. That's why I'd never seen her in the street. She never went out, except sometimes at night. She showed us once: covering her head with the shawl and holding a little torch, she scooted around the carpet pretending to weed the garden...the scene I already knew by heart.

Derek's dad was building a business for them, somewhere quite far off. I never knew where or what it was. He'd come home and stay for a few days, and then Derek would not appear in the street or in the library. I asked him why.

'Dad thinks we should do things together...He's not home often.'

'Things like?'

'Going interesting places...like museums, like concerts...'

I began to hate that Humber Hawk. Not only because it kept my friend away from me, but something much worse – I was in love. What can I say now, except repeat the words of Isaac Babel's story 'First Love': 'The love and jealousy of a ten-year-old boy are in every way the same as the love and jealousy of a grown-up.' And I would add: and perhaps more painful, since the ten-year-old has also the pain of knowing himself to be a child.

Every night I stood at my window with my light off and looked across the street – I saw her draw the curtains, and just once the shadow of her arms drew the mohair sweater over her head, and another night I climbed down our front porch and buried my best purple slate arrowhead in the little flower bed they'd made under their front window.

～

Time had come to start preparations for the Rose Queen festival, though this year many folk thought it would be the last. This was partly because TV was growing in popularity, and lots of people wanted to stay at home to watch sports programmes on Saturdays, and also because a new school was being built for us in Marshside. We had a new teacher, too. She asked us to suggest ideas for our class's boys' dance. We had never been asked before, and it seemed as though suddenly our *opinions* were beginning to matter! I made three suggestions – archers at Agincourt, Crusaders, or Spitfire pilots. But Strodger made just one suggestion – football, the Cup Tie!

'O that's a nice simple one, isn't it,' said Miss Hargreaves. 'And not very expensive for the costumes.' And everyone but for me and Derek Hesketh cheered. So the choice was made.

And in keeping with this new democratic spirit, Old Slater came wheeling a sort of post box into the classroom, festooned with red, white and blue crepe paper, and announced that this year we would all VOTE for the Rose Queen of our choice!

'Boys and girls, here in England, we are a free society, we are not like those Nazis and Communists. We all express our opinions in a vote! And you will now vote as well in this, your first election for our Rose Queen!' We almost found the courage to cheer, but Miss Hargreaves was quietly indicating that, instead, we should just applaud politely, and so we did. Nevertheless, we went home that day in an almost hysterical fit of universal joy.

All we could think of was VOTE, VOTE, VOTE...And all of our class had a single name in mind – Sarah Threlfall: she *would* be Rose Queen. It was inevitable. There was not another girl in the whole of Southport who could beat her!

Next day, each of us was given a slip of paper with a rubber stamp of authority in one corner. This, our Headmaster explained, was to prevent the detestable act of ballot-box stuffing: it was to be one person, one vote. We were given ten minutes to write the name of our choice and post it. We awaited the result with impatience, but when Old Slater did appear, it was to inform us that the result was a draw between two girls – Margaret Ball and Gloria Rimmer...Two girls, neither of whom we had ever heard of! And therefore a final decision would be made by tossing a coin. Mr Dobbins was called to perform the deed, and Margaret Ball was duly elected Rose Queen.

It was awful, outrageous! The girls took it well enough, whispering '*I could have guessed*' and suchlike among themselves, but we boys were in a towering passion, fuming with indignation and exasperation. Some were crying openly, unable to control their emotions. Worst of all was Strodger, standing under the Headmaster's window sobbing, shouting as best he could, 'LIAR...JUDAS...I KNOW YOU...I KNOW YOU NOW...NEVER TRUST YOU...NEVER NEVER AGAIN.' And so on until Mr Dobbins and Miss Hargreaves came out to try and control us and gather us together. When they succeeded, we learned the terrible truth: that morning, the school secretary had been dispatched to visit the parents of girls who, perhaps, could have been voted Rose Queen, and what she discovered was that only two girls in the village had parents able to afford the dress.

'It's like a wedding dress, you know,' Miss Hargreaves said. 'Terribly expensive!'

That truth didn't really satisfy us – there were mutterings and shouts. *Sir, what matters most, the girl or the dress?... Why can't we have two queens, sir, one for grown-ups with a dress and one for us just in her apron...just in her gaberdine?...Just in her own best dress? Sir?*

But I suppose we had learned something.

∾

One Saturday, coming home from the museum where I'd been trying my best to make sketches of various parts of the armour, Derek told me his mum had a favour to ask. I was thrilled, of course. We went round to the back door. She seemed much more than usually serious.

'Roy,' she said – *Roy*, in the voice that haunted my existence. 'Derek has told me you've been making armour from tin cans, Roy, and...I'd love to see it, Roy!'

My face burned. I was exposed, a child, a silly child. *I wasn't ready!*

'Please, Roy. Please...'

I tried to explain. I still had to learn soldering. I'd learned riveting from my Uncle Hugh but I still hadn't learned soldering. As soon as...Yes, I'd show it to her...

She fell to her knees in front of me, as I'd seen her do before with Derek, but now she seemed altogether more solemn.

'I'll beg!' she said.

I was dreadfully aware of the coarse matting under her knees. Slowly, she undid her braid and began letting out the plaits. *'Please...'*

I was lost. I ran home in a panic and began to fasten on my best bits: thighs, calves, upper arms, gorget... At least my elastic was black, so it didn't show. I carried the helm under my arm, as one should, and headed back – around Grandma, through the kitchen, out of the back door, across the yard, up the alley, and over the road... And thus I presented myself.

She had finished combing out her braids – and it was true: her hair fell to her knees. She held her head sideways as she pulled the comb through it, and it swayed like a dense skein of reddish silk thread. She glimpsed me standing in the doorway, gasped and dropped her comb, clapping both hands to her mouth.

'Oh!... Oh God! I *see...* I *see...'* Laughter convulsed her.

She apologised immediately, as always, as always. And then I lied: 'My idea for armour, because I suggested we should be Crusaders in the Rose Queen parade and it's hard to find armour... But now it's no use, because they want to be footballers.'

'Oh! That's such a pity, such nice armour...'

Did she believe me? Crusaders didn't wear plate armour... But she pretends. How complicated it was. Even then, I knew there were some advantages to being a child, along with the disadvantages. My main difficulty was finding ways to see her, to stay with her long enough. And Derek, too – he was still my best friend. It wasn't his fault that I'd fallen in love with his mother. He was still my friend, and all the rest had to be hidden from him, and though he was terribly perceptive, he never saw through my deception. At least, so I believe, though perhaps he was hiding something, too.

'It's just imagination, isn't it?' That's what she said. 'For Roy, it's his armour and his arrowheads...' And she looked at me quite differently than any grown-up had looked at me before. 'It's imagination!' she insisted.

'*You* imagine things, too, don't you, Mum?' Derek said. 'Tell Roy about the river...'

'Oh no!'

'Oh Mum, yes, please...'

And at last she told us about the river. It started in the carpet and led her into a world where she'd never been before. When she got there, she couldn't find her way back. All she could do was cry. '*But it's just a carpet...*' she said, now almost crying...'A carpet.'

'It's all right, Mum,' Derek said. 'You don't do it any more...'

When I went home, I threw my tin-can armour in the dustbin. I kept the helm – it looked so much like the helmet of Simon de Montfort, I couldn't part with it.

Always a drum roll to begin. Parents get to their feet. We all wait, standing at attention – footballers. Eric, over there, with the Morris Men and Morris Girls. They are stealing all eyes. The Banks Brass Band starts up – it's Grandma's favourite tune, the one she calls 'Th'Owd Hundert'. This is the only time our village sings as one, voices floating up slowly gathering together, louder and louder:

All people that on earth do dwell
Sing to the Lord with cheerful voice...

The Morris Men walk out towards the maypole. They untie the knots and set free the streamers. The music starts – Mr Dobbins has to keep winding the gramophone, or else they will be out of time. It's like that when our turn comes, and we have to kick the ball exactly in time to the tune. It's almost impossible. Only Mr Dobbins can get it just right!

The dance begins, and the boys weave the imaginary web. It's supposed to be a house, Eric said. When it's ready, the girls skip out in white dresses and chaplets of buttercups and daisies. At that, the parents start clapping. Some have tears running down their faces: they can't believe this will be the last time! They don't cry at us, though. Miss Hargreaves has done a good job of making us funny, so we get nowt but laughs!

Later, when the parents have gone home, we stay playing king-of-the-castle on the dais until dark. Some of our class girls join in, and we get a wonderful idea: we'll crown Sarah Threlfall on the dais. We run round finding chaplets that have fallen off, and we bow to her and say, 'Your Majesty Sarah.' So now she'll know that *she* was the real Rose Queen! But she doesn't seem to care – she just laughs us away and says, 'Don't be silly! I'm not a queen! I'm going to be the scullery maid!' Oh these girls...they get such daft ideas!

I hear Eric shouting for me, but I don't answer. I hide in the willows waiting to be last, the very last, to have the Rose Queen field to myself, so I can remember it, remember the way it was...then it will be mine forever.

On the way home I see Sarah walking ahead, and I run to catch up and then walk beside her along the churchyard wall. I want to say something brave. 'I voted for you,' I say. She smiles. 'We all voted for you' – and she smiles again.

But what really worries me...How can I love them both? When do I have to choose? When can I marry? These are the things I think about every night, looking out of my bedroom window.

∾

It must have been near the end of that summer. We took sandwiches and pop and went for a long day on the mere. I had a GPO notebook Dad had brought home, and my idea was to make maps in it when we found places that may have been islands. Where islands had left little hills, there may have been homesteads, and where there were homesteads, there must have been canoes. So we lay flat on our bellies, surveying around us, looking for rising ground. Those tracks were supposed to be private, but if anyone asked us what we were doing there, I used to say I was taking my Uncle Hugh his lunch. That was all right. Everyone knew Uncle Hugh – he was the area billiards champion!

We had a special place for our picnics, a little covert at the confluence of two dykes. Eric took me there at first, because it was his favourite spot to go fishing. That day, we saw that a dredger-crane had been at work, and had been left at the edge of the wood. After eating our lunch, we got inside and tried to understand how it worked. But we couldn't start it – 'There's always a key!' Derek said – so instead I began searching in the dredged piles of mud along the bank, hoping to find flints or other stone things from the bottom of the dyke. The water level was low after a fairly hot, dry summer, and I saw that the dredger had left a log partly sticking up. That was the kind of wood I was familiar with, black and striated – fossilised! I knew then it was no log. I jumped into the edge of the dyke and ran my hands along it, and wrapped my arms around it as far as I could reach. It was hollow . . . there were tapered sides, gunwales . . .

'It's a canoe!' I shouted. 'I can feel it . . . It's a dugout!'

Derek jumped down into the water and we both felt under it as far as possible. The truth was clear: 'It's true!' he shouted. 'We're not imagining it, it's a dugout canoe . . . CONGRATULATIONS, PROFESSOR! YOU'VE DONE IT!' We stood there, thigh-deep in the dyke in utter astonishment. It was real! Not childish, not imaginary – a prehistoric dugout canoe!

Under most circumstances, it would not seem possible for two ten-year-old boys to lift a canoe of fossilised wood from such a dyke and lay it on the bank. However, we did just that, and by mid-afternoon we were able to glory in the success of our labour. Needless to say, the dredger had done most of the hard part, but the rest we accomplished with a determination bordering on mania. It was in astonishingly good condition, much better than the canoe in the museum, though neither as long nor as wide.

A real find! I was determined to get to the museum before closing time. We rode fast down the bumpy lanes just in time to find him – the man with gold braid on his sleeves whom I had always thought of as the curator – just about to lock the doors. We poured out our story, but he seemed completely unimpressed.

'Those dugouts are heavy!' he said. 'Damned heavy! And I've already got one. What would it cost to get another one transported? And where would it go? There's no room for another...'

We were left in blank disbelief. He spoke as though you could get prehistoric canoes for tuppence!

'Let's go back,' Derek said. 'Let's hide it in the woods...'

It was late afternoon, and we were tired out. We saw them from the distance – a gang of lads, five of them, bigger than us, pushing our canoe towards the dyke. We stopped short of them.

'That's ours!' Derek shouted. 'We found it!'

'It's ours now!' one of them replied, and added: 'We'll fight you for it!'

'What d'you think you're doing?' I screamed.

'Putting it in the water. What d'you think?'

'But it'll sink. It isn't wood – it's fossilized, it's stone!'

'Get lost!' he replied. 'You're mad!'

And we watched as they heaved it back to the edge of the bank, and tipped it into the dyke, and saw like in a nightmare, excruciatingly slowly, our treasure drop out of sight.

'YOU STUPID...' No words were good enough. The gang of them stared at the water in disbelief, muttered quietly for a few moments, then mounted their bikes and rode off. They went towards Scarisbrick – lads I had never seen before and never saw again.

So the greatest event of my childhood folded itself away. I told no one, ever. But Derek's mum, next time I saw her, looked at me with a sort of helpless agony in her eyes, and said: 'Derek told me... That stupid man! That stupid, stupid man!'

I saw her only twice more – and finally learned her name. It was Bonfire Night, and for this once the bonfire was in our garden. We'd made a respectable effort of it, between us, collecting old furniture, smashing it up, piling it against the back fence.

She had promised to come. I crossed the road to bring her. She was wearing a plaid skirt, and her hair was gathered half-length. I knew the plaid: 'That's Hunting Stewart!' I said. She stopped in the middle of the road and stared at me – 'Roy!' she said.

It was fine! Grandma had made parkin, and we had a turnip lantern in the window. Mam and Dad stood together as always, though Dad lit the fireworks. Grandma had a chair by the yard gate. *She* stayed by herself, or hugged Derek if she could get hold of him. Dad went to light a giant pinwheel – 'Is it safe?' she said. 'Are you sure it's...' Dad gave her a queer look. He didn't know about her imagination. I lit some sparklers and did the usual things with them – everyone always pretends they burn, and everyone knows they don't.

'*NO!*'

She doubled over, covering her face, and began sobbing. Derek quickly pulled her hands down. 'Mum, it's only a sparkler! Look! They don't burn!' He grabbed it from me and passed it back and forth over his arm, his hands... '*It doesn't burn! See...*'

But she fled without a word, sobbing up the alley. Derek went, too, but came back alone.

'Too soft for this world!' Grandma said. 'Too soft by half!'

It was Grandma who found her one day, sitting on the kerb in Rufford Road, sobbing and covering her head with her shawl. Several people were trying to help, but she'd have nothing to do with them. Grandma said: 'She's my neighbour, let me to her... Now what's this about? Whatever's the matter?'

She told Grandma she was lost and couldn't find the way home. So Grandma told her not to be so silly. 'You're Phoebe Hesketh, aren't you? You know me, don't you? You know I live across the road, with Roy and Peg and Bob? Come on wi' me – take my arm and we'll go home... We'll go together.'

And she cried all the way, and then Grandma cried when she told the story, and Mam said: 'It doesn't bode well... not well at all.'

And I whispered, 'It's her imagination.'

The last glimpse of her – of *Phoebe* – was from their own back garden. It was winter. Derek had gone away somewhere with his dad, and I never saw lights in the front rooms, down or up. She could have been... lost somewhere. I was desperate to see her.

One evening after dark, I decided to creep down their passage into the garden to see whether she was in the back room. The garden was a mess of overgrown shrubs and long grass. I suppose it had never even been a garden. The dyke ran across behind. On hands and knees, I made my way round the side of the house until I could see through the windows. One room was lit – the back ground-floor room. And there she was, walking back and forth very quickly, from wall to wall, back and forth, back and forth.

I could make no sense of it. And then she stopped, she stopped dead, and in a single, swift movement she drew that pink mohair sweater up over her head, so that I saw...

Nothing! I wasn't there to see anything like that. No pink *thing*. As soon as something – the pink edge of something – became visible, I flung myself flat on my face into the weeds and lay there. I was ashamed. By the time I looked up, the light was off and the curtains were drawn shut upstairs.

∾

At last, Derek came home, and our activities resumed. We heard that a postman, out fishing on the marshes, had unearthed a pot of Roman coins while digging for worms, so we had a day planned to look for this place – we thought we could find the hole and look around the same area.

I came down into the kitchen quite early. Grandma was up already. I was heading straight for the back door. She grabbed me and held me back.

'It's no use looking for him,' she said. 'They've gone, they've a' gone. Yellow van took her off at the crack o' dawn, then your friend went with his dad in t'car...' I was stunned, in disbelief, still trying to get through the door. 'Don't go looking,' she said. 'There's no use.'

It was true. The windows were bare, the rooms empty. Everything had been taken away during the night. Grandma was *grateful* that I'd not seen them take her. I heard her tell my mother so. And Mam replied, 'We must thank the Lord for small mercies!'

So I would never know what happened, never know

what they did...never, never know. I created consolations. Soon I would be old enough to rescue her. I would just need a good sword, and I knew where I could get one – I would have to steal it, that's all! But first, I'd need to know where they'd taken her. Like the rest of my generation, I believed that Greaves' Hall, on the corner of Banks' Road opposite The Plough, was a real lunatic asylum, and the poor souls who lived within had been transported there in yellow vans to spend the rest of their lives in a nightmare of misery. Two or three times a week, we used to see them being shepherded along the pavements of Preston Road by their keepers, and they made strange sounds and little gestures to us children, luring us into their orbits. Could she have been taken there?

A few days after the event, I was driven by my despair to find out. I dressed, as I thought, in my most formal clothes, and through my belt I thrust our fire-poker, which in truth was, or had been, a respectable weapon – a German bayonet someone had brought back from the trenches in 1918. The point was missing from all those nights stoking our kitchen fire, but I thought it looked threatening nevertheless.

How can I admit it? Did I really go to the front entrance and bang on that huge door, and hear numerous locks and bolts rattling and scraping? A nurse appeared – a woman in a white apron. A voice behind her said, 'Who is it?' and she answered, 'Goodness me! It's a little boy...And he's got a sword! What do you want, love?'

'Can I see Mrs Phoebe Hesketh, please?'

(Voice behind: 'Is it a real sword?')

'He wants Phoebe Hesketh...Yes, it's real.'

'Tell him there's no Phoebe Hesketh living here, and don't let him in with that sword!'

'Come in if you want, love, but leave that thing in the umbrella rack!'

'If she's not here, I'll go home. But where did they take her?'

The other nurse comes into view now, and peers at me with great curiosity. 'Is it your mother, darling?'

'No she's my friend's mother. They took her away day before yesterday.'

'O dear! Well, love, they don't bring anyone here nowadays...You can come in and see for yourself.'

'Well, where do they take them?'

They both shook their heads. 'You could ask her doctor, if you know who he is.'

'OK. Thanks...Good night.'

Yes, I could ask the doctor, any doctor, they must know!

'Please, sir, where do they take women who go mad?' Why wouldn't he just tell me? He might say: 'And why are you asking this question, my boy?' And then I'll answer, 'My friend wants to know where they took his mother, but he's too scared to ask. So I have to ask for him.' Then, surely, he'll tell me. 'Brave boy,' he'll say, 'to ask such a question for your friend!' And then he'll write the address on a piece of paper and hand it to me. That's the way it will happen.

And home I went, into the dark. I went past our school, the churchyard wall, the Rose Queen field, the street where Sarah lived. And all the time I heard a voice saying, *'Well, you tried! You did try, didn't you!'* It was Derek's voice. Perhaps it was a dream after all, one thing in all these vivid memories that I'm ever-so-slightly unsure of. For years, I thought it was true. Every time I went past Greaves' Hall I'd look down the avenue to that front door, and remember the whole thing. One day, I realised that the nurse – the first woman who came to the door – was the same person who used to work in the museum...Or that was the woman she became.

∼

These memories became my secrets, and I never spoke of them, never! That winter, we had thick ice in the playground. Every class made a slide, boys' slides and girls' slides, criss-crossing everywhere. Then at lunchtime, the caretaker came out with a bag of salt and ruined our fun. The boys went back to playing football, and I went back to walking round and round with my hands in my pockets.

A new lad joined the game, but he didn't seem to know which side he was on – he scored twice, once for each side.

'Which side are you on?' someone shouted, and he replied, 'I don't care...I'll play for both sides!' So they banned him from the game. He fought back, but it was no use. He gave up, and walked towards me, sniffling.

'Why aren't you playing?' he asked.

'I'm banned...'

'Why, what for?'

'For flapping my arms when I run.'

'What's wrong with that?'

'They say it's against the rules.'

He nodded, put his arm round my shoulder, and we walked slowly away.

'Rules!' he said, lifting his other arm up into the air in a grand gesture. 'What care we for rules!'

His name was Barry Bartlett Bold, and soon he was my best friend. 'Well, why not!' a voice whispered. 'Why not, until you're older…'

14 July 2018
Aubin-St-Vaast

The Three Legs: tide marker, Crossens Marsh

AFTERWORD

Writing *Simple Annals*

During the summer of 1969 I was living in Brooklyn and finishing some writings towards an MFA. I had been in America as a Fulbright Scholar for two years, writing mostly short fiction and translations from French. I hoped to finish with a short novel, a family saga about my mother's parents, working-class folk from the Lancashire coast near Southport. I had lived with that grandmother through my childhood, and I felt a strong duty and desire to write about her life. I always wrote at night, and upon going to bed I left a sheet of paper rolled into my typewriter in case I was struck by some idea, image, or dream in the middle of the night. One morning, I noticed some typing on that sheet of paper, though I had not the slightest memory of having been out of bed to write it. It seemed, also, that I had not opened my eyes. The typing was an incoherent jumble of apparently unconnected phrases about fire, explosions, soldiers, and railway lines. Hours passed before I began to realise that I had dreamed of an actual experience – a bombing raid on a railway line while my mother was taking me to visit my father at an Air Force base in Leighton Buzzard. Image by image, that memory grew over the following days into a fully detailed panorama inside a crowded railway carriage. I wrote a description of the scene, and it became the first of my *First Images,* first 'annal' of my *Simple Annals*. That raid happened a few days before my third birthday. My mother later told me that those soldiers were Americans, and they had covered us with their greatcoats in case of a bomb strike near our carriage.

It now would seem that my dreams at that time caused the flow of these memories which had never before surfaced. Mostly, however, they did not have the dramatic force of bombing raids. (Though there was a dog-fight once over our cul-de-sac, and Uncle Hugh's nightly mission to run around the village in his Home Guard helmet, dumping buckets of water on doodle-bugs. Although the village was never bombed, Liverpool docks were only a few miles away.) There are a few life-changing events in my subject matter, such as my father's return home from war, but mostly my memories, my images, were of homely events, inconsequential conversations, daily trivia. I did not need to imagine narrative detail nor the family language. Every word returned to me in its natural dialect.

I made some rules for myself. First, I decided not to deliberately search my past looking for such events, and whenever I did remember something from that time, I would record it no matter how unimportant or even silly it may have seemed. My assumption was that if I had carried such memories in my head unknowingly, they must all have deserved their place in there. I never attempted to discover a chronology among them; in fact, I soon began deliberately to avoid one. Rhythm became my organising principle. And finally, I invented nothing – NO fiction!

I have often been asked which writers influenced this work. The answer really is none. Both content and style grew out of dreams and memories and the voices of my real-life characters. However, I did read and came to admire some special books whose authors seem to have gone through a similar process, some of these suggested to me by writers who had read some of my pieces. W. S. Merwin, for example, suggested that I should read Isaac Babel and Bruno Schulz; Edward Dahlberg told me I must go out at once and buy *The Autobiography of Emanuel Carnevali*, Kay Boyle's amalgam edition of Carnevali's only book, originally published under the title *A Hurried Man* (in Paris, 1925), which had been long unavailable. The wonderful writings of H.D., *Bid Me To Live* and *The Gift*, I discovered for myself. However, I had written several of the pieces in the First Part of *Simple Annals* before reading any of these.

The first publication of some of this small book – 21 pages to be exact, under the title *First Images* – took place during May 1980, at our own private press, Embers Handpress. It was our fifth publication. Just 126 copies were printed and circulated, mostly among friends and relatives. A few were sold through bookshops from time to time, at about £5. The first sentence of the colophon states 'This is the first of three texts to be collectively entitled *Simple Annals*.' I seem to have been very sure of that, though until now this 'collective' edition has never appeared. A few pages were printed in magazines, perhaps twice or thrice during all those years. One was included in a creative writing textbook at the University of Minnesota, edited by the poet Michael Dennis Browne; another, entitled 'A Wartime Sequence', appeared in the international literary review *Constellation* of the University of Maryland (2007), edited by Christine Leche. The longest of these early versions, and first to be entitled *First Images*, was intended for a magazine to be published in Paris and printed in Brighton, but went missing forever between those two destinations. Copies from such small runs were handed around. There were even some imitations – one of which won a gold medal! Recently, copies have been returned to me, for the saddest of reasons. If it is ever to be completed, surely the time has come.

I have tried several times to add more material in the same style and spirit as that first publication, but I always felt that I was producing an imitation of myself. I stuck to my 'no fiction' rule, but authentic memories of my early years did not continue to flow, either in dream or memory. Then, in February 2018, I got up one morning and I felt a strong urge to start writing. And once again, I found forgotten images awakening, and a spirit took over. I could hardly tell my new images from the early ones – at least, I had to check, to be sure that I was not simply repeating an old memory. I continued writing until I reached a chronological limit of my interest – I did not wish to write about my life post-puberty, where one inevitably rejects the little 'inconseqential' images, and adult values take over. I must apologise to those friends who keep urging me to continue 'until you left home'. I can only assure them that by those latter days I had become unworthy of the effort! Time to return to fiction, or to other subjects. My *Annals* end a few days before my eleventh birthday.

ROY WATKINS

13 February 2020
Aubin-St-Vaast, France